SPINDRIFT

A collection of
Poems, Songs and Stories
for young children

Wynstones Press

Published by
Wynstones Press
Ruskin Glass Centre
Wollaston Road
Stourbridge
West Midlands DY8 4HE.
England.
Email: info@wynstonespress.com
Website: www.wynstonespress.com

First Published 1978 by Wynstones Press
Second edition with music 1983
Fully revised third edition 1999. Reprinted 2005, 2010.

Editors: Jennifer Aulie and Margret Meyerkort

Cover illustration by David Newbatt

Typeset by Wynstones Press.
Printed in EU.

British Library CIP data available.

ISBN 0 946206 50 3

Spindrift

This is one in a series of 6 books:
Spring, Summer, Autumn, Winter, Spindrift and Gateways.

The four seasonal books comprise a wide selection of poems, songs and stories appropriate to the time of year, including much material for the celebration of festivals.

Spindrift contains verses and songs describing the world of daily work and practical life, together with a selection of stories from around the world.

Gateways comprises verses and songs for the Morning time, the Evening time and to accompany a variety of traditional Fairytales, together with poems, songs and stories for the celebration of Birthdays.

Warmest thanks to all who have contributed to and supported this work: parents, teachers and friends from Steiner Waldorf Schools in Australia, Britain, Canada, Eire, Estonia, New Zealand, Norway, South Africa and the United States. Grateful thanks also to publishers who have permitted the use of copyright material, acknowledgements for which are at the end of the volume.

INDEX

Indexes of first lines

POEMS

5

SONGS

Index of titles
STORIES

The Value of Music in the Life of the Young Child

Free Play in a Waldorf Kindergarten. It is a winter morning: the twenty children are busy with their work. The youngest, three- and four-year-olds, are helping the teacher chop apples for snack; some five-year-old girls are taking care of their "children" in the doll corner; next to them are a group of five-year-old boys and girls who are sitting at a round table polishing stones, grating chestnuts and chatting together. In the centre of the room an observant and energetic four-year-old boy is directing the six-year-olds in the construction of a snowplough: tables are stacked on each other, chairs turned upside down and leaned against the tables for the front part of the plough. A large basket of chestnuts is balanced on top of the plough. The chestnuts are grit and salt, to be scattered later on the ploughed streets. The room is small and the noise level is moderately high.

Underneath the windows, on the carpet where the children have a free space to build up scenes and play with standing puppets and animals, a six-year-old girl sits, absorbed in her work. She has laid out a forest of pine cones, which stands on the banks of a river of blue cloth. Stepping stones allow the poor shepherd boy, who lives at the edge of the forest, to cross the river and wind his way to the castle gates nearby . . . The princess, leaning out of her tower, sees him coming and calls down to him . . .

As she lays out the scene, the girl accompanies her actions with narrative, speaking in a soft tone, sometimes almost whispering to herself. When the puppets begin to live in the scene her voice changes, becoming more sung than spoken, the pitch of her spoken voice being taken over by her singing voice. Her recitative is not sing-song rhythmic, but the rhythm freely moves with the intention of the shepherd boy as he jumps from stone to stone. The pitch of the girl's voice is a colourful monotone: the pitch remains much the same, but the tone colour is enlivened through the intensity and quality of the words as the shepherd crosses the stream. There are moments when a word is spoken, then the narrative is sung again.

When the shepherd arrives at the castle gates, the princess calls down to him from her high tower. She is far away, and the girl reaches up with her voice to the distant place where the princess lives, and sings her greetings down to the shepherd. The girl's voice is high now, but the intervals she sings are not large, they are between a third and a fifth. The high pitch of her voice, although it is not loud, has attracted some of the five-year-olds: several come over to the rug and lie on their stomachs, watching the play unfold. The shepherd now tells the princess of his wish that she come down and go with him. The simple recitative changes to a declamatory aria: a melody of several different tones arises, moving stepwise, the girl's voice becomes more intense as the shepherd pleads his cause. There is little repetition in the melody, but the movement contained in it provides a musical mood which waits expectantly for the princess's reply . . .

In the meantime, the snowplough has already cleared quite a few streets. It has come back to make a second round to scatter the grit and salt . . . The four-year-olds slicing apples jump up from the table. The noise of all those chestnuts hitting a wooden floor is so wonderful, they want to join the fun! The "mothers" putting their children to bed are angry that the snowplough has woken up their little ones, now the babies are crying . . . Some of the children polishing stones and grating chestnuts try throwing their stones and chestnuts on the floor – what a good idea, it makes a lovely *cracking* sound . . .

. . . the five-year-olds listening to the play hold their breaths as the princess agrees to go with the shepherd but he must first ask permission from her father, the king . . . The princess's instructions are sung to him in a melody of seconds with a strong, definite rhythm . . .

An observer can hardly believe that the chestnut-strewn chaos in the other half of the room (which the teacher is quickly helping to put right again) does not seem to penetrate the sheath of peacefulness which surrounds the puppet play. The children gathered around it show no sign that anything else in the room has taken place . . .

At the successful conclusion of the play, the children watching it lie still. The girl covers the scene with a cloth and sings in a half-whispering tone a farewell to the story of the shepherd and the princess. As her voice fades, there is a moment of absolute silence. Then the five-year-olds run back to the polishing table and the girl goes to the teacher to ask how long it will be until snack.

This description of a six-year-old girl's singing contains many elements of what has come to be called "Mood of the Fifth" music: the singing follows the rhythm of speech; melodies are simple, moving within intervals of seconds and thirds – sometimes as large as a fifth, rarely larger; melodies are often sung on one tone, the pitch taken from the speaking voice; the melodies are not written in major or in minor keys and have an open-ended feel to them. Above all is the mood of the music: when sung properly it seems to reach out and enfold the children in a protective sheath which has a quality of stillness and peace, although the children themselves may be active within it.

This music is a musical expression of an experience which is striven for in all aspects of Waldorf Education. It is difficult to describe in words, perhaps: "I am centred in my activity," "My thinking, feeling and willing are in balance." One feels deeply united with a task, at peace and yet still active. The young child finds this mood in play. S/he is deeply engaged in an activity which is then no longer interesting when the activity is over. The moment of silence at the end of the play was not a moment of reflection, but a moment which allowed the activity of watching the play to come to a complete end before the next task could engage the children's attention.

The broader context of this musical experience should be noted: the kindergarten just described is one where mood-of-the-fifth music was not cultivated by the teacher. The children learned only traditional children's songs and games which were sung in strict rhythm, and with major or minor key melodies. The six-year-old girl experienced similar music at home.

Yet the girl's singing is not an isolated or unusual musical event. Such singing can often be heard when a child's attention is fully engaged in his/her play. We grown-ups tend to dismiss such fragments of melody as noise, or incomplete attempts by the child to sing our music, not listening closely enough to discover the innate coherence of the child's activity. Too often well-meaning adults try to "correct" the pitch which is too high, or the rhythm which is irregular, and slowly wall in a living musicality with "proper" songs . . . Sooner or later, often at puberty, an attempt is made at breaking through these walls, as the pounding beat of popular music has long suggested.

The use of "Mood of the Fifth" music in the kindergarten encompasses two considerations. It is first of all a path of musical development for the adult, which schools his/her musical perception and ability so that s/he is able to participate in a musicality which the children *already possess.* This musicality may, for many reasons, lie dormant or misshapen within an individual child or group of children. Through the adult's use of Mood of the Fifth s/he can reawaken and bring back into movement the musicality which is so essential for the full development of the child's soul life. (To be labelled "unmusical" or "tone deaf" causes deep, lingering wounds to the child's self esteem. There are unfortunately many adults who can attest to the truth of this statement out of their own experience.)

Mood of the Fifth music can also help the adult to establish an additional point of contact with the child which shows him/her that the adult *understands.* One of the rewards of working with young children is surely the open look of delight on a child's face when s/he hears a story, plays a game, experiences something which pleases him/her. The look of delight means more, however, than just "I like that." On a deeper level it expresses the child's trust in the adult: "You know who I am, and what you offer me is that which I am searching for with my deepest intentions. I can follow you."

The present day task of the Waldorf Kindergarten is primarily a therapeutic one. It provides children with basic experiences which they need for healthy development, overcoming deficiencies which often occur today in the first years of life. A very large part of these experiences are sensory, as the development of the physical senses (touch, balance, etc.) lays the foundation for the later unfolding of the spiritual capacities (thinking, speech, etc.). The kindergarten is not a mirror of our daily lives, but an extract of the many activities, distilled to their essence. This provides a simplicity and basic necessity for the content of kindergarten life which the child can understand and imitate wholeheartedly. The meaningful activity around the child awakens his/her interest in the world, and this interest becomes the mainspring of later learning.

In the arts the materials presented to the child are restricted to essentials, and with these the child's imagination has free rein. This can be clearly seen, for example, in painting: the three primary colours are used – red, yellow and blue. The children are given watercolours, a large wet sheet of paper and a broad brush to paint with. The materials themselves preclude any precise drawing, colours flow into one another, sometimes mixing, sometimes remaining pure side by side. There is no right or wrong way of using the colours, the expansive, fiery or cool moods of the colours themselves guide the child's brush. The medium of water enables the child's soul to breathe freely in the movement of colour with the brush. If only the paper were bigger s/he could paint on and on . . .

Music can be approached in a similar way. Here as well the materials can be restricted so that the *activity* becomes of foremost importance. Only five different tones of our twelve tone system are used:

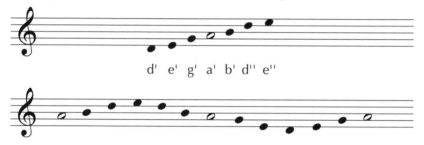

d' e' g' a' b' d'' e''

When a children's harp or lyre is used, the strings are tuned to pure fifths (like a violin's open strings) rather than the tempered intervals of the piano. The songs are not written in major or minor keys, but tend to circle around the middle tone, a'. The rhythm is free, either gently swinging (3 or 6 beats) or walking (2 or 4 beats), but the movement of the music takes its impulse from the words and seeks to accompany its inner content.

This style of music making lends itself wonderfully to the activities of circle time where movement, the spoken word and song freely flow from one to the other, just as the three basic colours do in painting. Teachers who have worked with Mood of the Fifth music in the classroom also know of its effectiveness in creating moments where the attention of all of the children is engaged, enabling a special mood to arise, whether in a puppet play, grace before meal, etc.

Newcomers to this music may at first experience difficulty in hearing the melodies or finding an inner connection to them. Others may have trouble finding the beginning pitch or singing the songs as high as they are written. None of these difficulties should be considered unsolvable problems.

Over time, the practice of Music of the Fifth songs often leads to a good sense of pitch. The voice gradually learns the placement of the tones, and the reduced number of tones make sight-singing possible even for the "unmusical" person.

Difficulty in reaching the higher notes (d″, e″), which lie within traditional singing range of soprano and altos, can be due to breathing which is too shallow, as well as to the false idea that high notes are more difficult to sing and require greater effort. In the long run, the question of extending the vocal range is best addressed by an experienced teacher. But those without a teacher can still consider the following: the vocal range can be affected by physical movement. Often much can be accomplished by accompanying a song with large, simple, physical gestures. This helps free the breathing, allowing greater ease in reaching notes which are "too high." The songs can be practised with movement until the feeling of vocal mobility is secure. Then the outward movement can gradually become smaller and disappear altogether, all the while maintaining the inner freedom of movement in the voice.

An essential guide for adults who wish to find a path into the experience of Mood of the Fifth music can be found in Julius Knierim's *Songs in the Mood of the Fifth (Quintenlieder)*. This succinct and clearly written booklet describes, with simple exercises and musical examples, a path which really can be taken by all who have a sincere interest in further development of their musical abilities. By working with the suggestions contained in Julius Knierim's essay, the serious student can develop capacities which not only lead him/her into the musical world of the young child, but can help build a new relationship to traditional classical music, and to al further musical development.

Rudolf Steiner, in discussing music for the young child, spoke of the great importance of the Quintenstimmung = *Mood* of the Fifth. The suggestions mentioned in this article, and most especially in Dr. Knierim's book, are guideposts by which adults may find the way into this mood. They are not the mood itself. Individual observation, experimentation, and practice are the means by which the letter of the law may be enlivened by its spirit.

The goal of these booklets is to offer immediate practical help in working with young children. It is for this reason that a variety of musical styles is included. All songs (as well as stories and verses) have proved their worth in Waldorf kindergartens or other settings with young children. Some traditional tunes with new words have been included, and many traditional rhymes have been set to new melodies (either pentatonic or Mood of the Fifth). Familiar children's songs have been excluded for the most part because these are readily available in other collections. Most songs are set in D-pentatonic. This is done for pedagogical as well as practical reasons (see references). Experience has shown that many teachers and parents who wish to consciously address music-making with the young child are often just those who are themselves struggling with their own musical education. With most songs written in D-pentatonic mode (which are tones of a Choroi flute or children's harp, and are easy to play on a traditional recorder), it is hoped that the initial difficulties with note reading and transposition will be eased. The use of bar lines and time signatures varies, showing new possibilities of notation. Some songs have traditional time signatures, others have only a 3 or 4 at the beginning to indicate a more swinging or walking rhythm. The absence of bar lines leaves the singer free to determine the musical phrasing according to the rhythm of the words and their sense. Commas indicate a slight pause, or point of rest.

Jennifer Aulie

References:

Knierim, Julius. *Songs in the Mood of the Fifth 'Quintenlieder'.*
ISBN: 0 945803 14 1 (Rudolf Steiner College Press, California)

Steiner, Rudolf. *The Study of Man.*
ISBN: 0 85584 187 8 (Rudolf Steiner Press, England)

Steiner, Rudolf. *The Inner Nature of Music and the Experience of Tone.*
ISBN 0 88010 074 5 (Steiner Books, Massachusetts)

HOUSE-WARMING

Blessing on this room of ours,
Blessing on the garden flowers,
Blessing on the birds and trees,
On the butterflies and bees.
Blessing on the dolls and toys,
On our quietness and noise.
Blessing on the children dear,
On the grown-ups who come here.
Blessing on our work and play –
God be with us all each day.

N. Foster

Bless - ings on ___ the blos - som,

Bless - ings on ___ the root, ___

Bless - ings on the leaf and stem,

Bless - ings on the fruit. ___

Softly quiet falls upon us, fills us with its grace,
Folded ev'ry hand is resting, peace on ev'ry face.
In the quiet, hushed and tender, strife at once departs.
May the Dove of Peace be resting ever in our hearts!

A. Riley

M. L. Channer   M. L. Channer

Sun - light, Sun - light, shin - ing on my
Sun - light, Sun - light, in my ear you
Sun - light, Sun - light, touch me with your

paint - ing mak - ing col - ours
whis - per all the se - crets
rain - bow, I can feel your

like the shin - ing dew.
of the world you know.
dark - ness and your light.

FOR PAINTING

There's a bridge of wondrous light
Filled with colours shining bright:
Red and orange, yellow, green,
The fairest colours ever seen,
Blue and violet, magic rose:
Down from heaven to earth it goes.

M. Meyerkort   *J. Knierim*

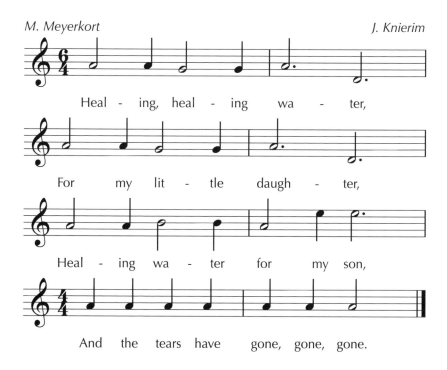

Heal - ing, heal - ing wa - ter,

For my lit - tle daugh - ter,

Heal - ing wa - ter for my son,

And the tears have gone, gone, gone.

1. Hark! There's a tattle-tale,
    Hiding in the clover;
    Katy-did, Katy-did,
    Over and over.

2. How did she find it out?
    Tell me how she knew so;
    Katy-did, Katy-did,
    Why did she do so?

Mother's washing, Mother's washing,
Rub, rub, rub.
Picked up Johny's little shirt
And put it in the tub.

Mother's washing, Mother's washing,
Scrub, scrub, scrub.
Picked up Mary's little frock
And put it in the tub.

Mother's washing, Mother's washing,
Wring, wring, wring.
Picked up Tommy's little coat
And hung it on some string.

Mother's finished, Mother's finished,
Hip hooray!
Now we'll have our clothes all clean
To wear for school today.

1. Mama, oh, mama, come wash my face;
   Wash my face, come wash my face;
   Mama, oh, mama, come wash my face;
   And make me nice and clean-o.

2. Daddy, oh, daddy, come fix my shoe;
   Fix my shoe, come fix my shoe;
   Daddy, oh, daddy, come fix my shoe;
   And polish nice and clean-o.

3. Sister, oh, sister, come bathe my back;
   Bathe my back, come bathe my back;
   Sister, oh, sister, come bathe my back;
   And make it nice and clean-o.

4. Clean-o clean, yes, clean-o clean;
   Clean-o clean, yes, clean-o clean;
   Scrubity scrubity and rubby dub dubbity;
   And make it nice and clean-o.

5. Brother, oh, brother, come wash my hair;
   Wash my hair, come wash my hair;
   Brother, oh, brother, come wash my hair;
   And make it nice and clean-o.

6. Granny, oh, granny, come wash my feet;
   Wash my feet, come wash my feet;
   Granny, oh, granny, come wash my feet;
   And make them nice and clean-o.

7. Sweetie, oh, sweetie, come smell of me now;
   Smell of me now, come smell of me now;
   Sweetie, oh, sweetie, come smell of me now;
   Don't I smell nice and clean-o?

W. Guthrie

1. Stretch the line from pole to pole, taut and tight.
    Wipe it carefully my dears, clean and white.
    Set the basket on the grasses,
    Shake the linen, now my lasses,
    Dry it in the blazing sun, warm and bright.

2. Hang the linen on the line, so and so.
    Evenly along the line make it go.
    Blows the wind, the naughty Rover,
    Drags the linen thro' the clover,
    You will help to dry it so, blow, wind, blow.

                                    A. Riley

When I come in from outdoor play
I take my boots off right away.
I set them by the door just so.
Then off my cap and mittens go.
Zip down my coat and snowpants too,
And hang them up when I am through.
I'm a helper, don't you see?
Helping's fun, as fun can be.

First I loosen mud and dirt
And then I rub them clean.
For shoes in such a dreadful sight
Never should be seen.
Next I spread the polish on
And then I let it dry.
I brush and brush and brush and brush,
How those shoes shine! OH, MY!

My Wellington boots go
Thump-thump, thump-thump,
My leather shoes go
Pit-pat, pit-pat,
My woolly slippers
Make no sound at all.

L. McCrea

We polish the window, the knife and the floor,
We polish the grate, the plate and the door,
We polish the fork, the spoon, ev'ry tin,
Till ev'rything shines like a silver pin.

Sing a song of washing-up,
Water hot as hot,
Cups and saucers, plates and spoons,
Dishes such a lot.
Work the dishmop round and round,
Wash them clean as clean.
Polish with a dry white cloth,
How busy we have been.

E. Gould

Ohhh – a churning we will go,
A churning we will go.
We'll take the cream
And shake it so,
And get the butter, OHHHHH !!!

Chop, chop, choppity-chop,
Cut off the bottom,
And cut off the top.
What there is left we will
Put in the pot;
Chop, chop, choppity-chop.

Mummy has scissors, snip, snip, snip;
Mummy has cotton, stitch, stitch, stitch.
Mummy has buttons, one, two, three;
She's making a dress,
Just for me!

G. Moore

One busy housewife sweeping up the floor,
Two busy housewives polishing the door,
Three busy housewives washing baby's socks,
Four busy housewives winding up the clocks,
Five busy housewives washing out the broom,
Six busy housewives tidying the room,
Seven busy housewives cleaning out the sink,
Eight busy housewives giving puss a drink,
Nine busy housewives stirring up the stew,
Ten busy housewives with nothing else to do.

(Children like to invent suitable mimes to accompany the words.)

K. Bartlett

Nelly Bly! Nelly Bly!
Bring the broom along,
We'll sweep the kitchen clean, my dear,
And have a little song.
Poke the wood, my lady-love,
And make the fire burn,
And while I take the banjo down,
Just give the mush a turn.

S. C. Foster

I help my mother.
I sweep the floor.
I dust the table.
I run to the store.
I help her beat the eggs,
And sift flour for cake.
Then I help her eat
All the good things she makes.

There are many things that I can do:
I can comb my hair and lace my shoe,
I can wash my hands and wash my face,
I can put my toys and blocks in place.

1. My mother called to me,
    And this is what she said,
    "Go down to the store,
    And buy a loaf of bread,
    And buy a loaf of bread."

    I danced down so happily,
    So very, very snappily,
    My mother sent me out,
    To buy a loaf of bread.

2. The storekeeper listened,
    And this is what he said,
    "Let's go to the baker,
    And get the loaf of bread,
    And get the loaf of bread."

    Chorus

3. We talked to the baker,
    And this is what he said,
    "The miller has the flour,
    For to bake the bread,
    Yes, for to bake the bread."

    Chorus

4. We went to the miller,
    In his mill so neat,
    "Go down to the farmer,
    For to get the wheat,
    Yes, for to get the wheat."

    Chorus

5. We came to the farmer,
    A-milking of his cow,
    He sent us to the blacksmith,
    For to get a plough,
    Yes, for to get a plough.

    Chorus

6. The farmer ploughed the field,
   The wheat it grew so high,
   He took it to the miller,
   When it was nice and dry,
   When it was nice and dry.

   Chorus

7. The miller ground the wheat,
   Until it was so fine,
   He put it in a sack,
   And sewed it up with twine,
   And sewed it up with twine.

   Chorus

8. While the baker made the dough,
   We went to get the coal,
   A miner dug it out
   Of a dark and spooky hole,
   A dark and spooky hole.

   Chorus

9. The dough was kneaded well,
   The coal was glowing red,
   The baker put in the dough,
   And soon it came out bread,
   And soon it came out bread.

   Chorus

10. The storekeeper wrapped it,
    And gave it straight to me,
    I took it home to mother,
    As proud as I could be,
    As proud as I could be.

    Chorus

P. Lancourt

BOW VERSES

Tiptoe, tiptoe,
Let us tie a rabbit bow.
Take an end in either hand
Tie the two quite tightly.
Bend them into rabbit ears,
Fasten them quite rightly.
Tiptoe, tiptoe,
We have tied a rabbit bow,
Laces fastened firm and neat,
Happy shoes on happy feet.

Tiptoe, tiptoe,
Let us make a rabbit bow.
Bend the ears and tie them neat.
Tip toe out, on happy feet.

L Charter

Little Betty Blue
Has a button on her shoe
But she's too fat to button it
So what can Betty do?
She can ask her brother Paul
Who is rather thin and small.
Then he will come and button it
Without a fuss at all.

A. C. Herbertson

We know how to tie our shoe.
We take the loop and poke it through.
It's hard to make it stay,
Because the thumb gets in the way.

Visitor:	Good morning, dear neighbour, how are you today?
Hostess:	Good morning! Good morning!
Visitor:	Do enter I pray! I'll enter a moment, no longer I dare.
Hostess:	Come into my parlour and please take a chair.
Visitor:	I hope you are well and your family too!
Hostess:	Quite finely, I thank you, and how do you do?
Visitor:	The weather is lovely, I really must go.
Hostess:	I beg you stay longer! What hurries you so?
Visitor:	I really must go, tho' I gladly would stay.
Hostess:	I hope you will come again some other day.
Visitor:	You come to see me, yes, you really must try.
Hostess:	So glad to have seen you! Good-bye, dear, good-bye!

A. Riley

Here's a cup
And here's a cup,
And there's a pot of tea.
Pour a cup,
And pour a cup,
And have a drink with me.

Bread is a lovely thing to eat.
God bless the barley and the wheat.
A lovely thing to breathe is air.
God bless the sunshine everywhere.
Earth is a lovely place to know.
God bless the folk that come and go.
Alive's a lovely thing to be.
Giver of life we say: Bless Thee.

H. M. Sarson

Mix a pancake – stir a pancake –
Pop it in a pan.
Fry a pancake – toss a pancake –
Catch it if you can!

I am making cookie dough,
Round and round the beaters go.
Add some flour from a cup,
Stir and stir the batter up.
Roll them, cut them, nice and neat,
Put them on a cookie sheet.
Bake them, count them, 1, 2, 3.
Serve them to my friends for tea.

Stirring batter, stirring batter,
Stir it so it does not spatter.
Round about the bowl is right,
White and gold and gold and white
Winds itself and finds itself
And smooth and sticky binds itself.
Patient stirring makes the cake
Which the baker's man can bake.

Make a tender piecrust,
Roll it very thin,
Put it in a pie pan,
With some cherries in,
Have the oven just right,
Trim it round about,
It will be delicious
When you take it out!

K. C. Goddard

1. Sugar and spice,
   Raisins and rice,
   Milk from the dairy,
   Give them to Mary;
   Mary will stir,
   Leave it to her.

2. Easy to make,
   Easy to bake,
   Very nutritious,
   Very delicious,
   Pudding to eat,
   Oh, what a treat.

Slice, slice, the bread looks nice.
Spread, spread butter on the bread.
On the top put jam so sweet,
Now it's nice for us to eat.

1. Baker, mix a penny loaf,
   Build a fire to bake it;
   Keep your oven all a-glow,
   That's the way to make it.

2. Baker, baker have a care,
   When you bake a show-cake;
   Watch your oven all the time,
   Lest you get a dough cake.

3. Baker, mix a fancy cake,
   Full of nuts and spices;
   When it's done we'll take a knife,
   Cut it into slices.

J. Aulie

1. Pat - a - cake, Pat - a - cake, ba - ker's man,

2. Bake me a cake as fast as you can.

Pat it and prick it and mark it with a "B", **3.** And

put it in the o - ven for ba - by and me.

Suggested directions:

1. *Any number of children – can be mother and her one small child – walk around freely and individually.*
2. *Then stand still and walk a little towards each other, or towards a centre and do patting action.*
3. *Then stretch flat hands out to put imaginary cake into oven.*

Mix the batter,
Stir the batter,
Shake some flour in.
Mix the batter,
Stir the batter,
Place it in a tin.
Sprinkle little raisins on.
Pop batter in to bake.
Open wide the oven door,
And out comes a cake!

36

Sing a song of mince meat
Currants, raisins, spice,
Apples, sugar, nutmeg,
Everything that's nice.
Stir it with a ladle,
Wish a little wish,
Drop it in the middle
Of your well-filled dish.
Stir again for good luck,
Pack it all away,
Tied in little jars and pots
Until Christmas Day.

E. Gould

Tinkle, tinkle, tinkle: 'tis the muffin man you see.
Tinkle, tinkle, tinkle says his little bell.
Any crumpets, any muffins, any cakes for tea.
Crumpets, muffins, cakes I have, plenty here to sell.

A. Hawkshawe

The farmer gave us golden grain
For us to grind and grind.
Now it's flour brown and white,
Soft and very fine.
Add the water, yeast and honey,
Mix it with our hands.
When it's soft and not too runny
Let it stand and stand.
Shape the dough into a loaf.
Put it in to cook.
When it's crusty, crisp and brown
We will have a look.

A. Clark

1. The milk wagon's horse goes clop, clop, clop,
   At all of the houses he makes a stop,
   He starts on his round at half-past four,
   The bottles are early outside the door.

2. The sound of the wagon goes clink, clink, clink,
   It brings you the milk that you drink, drink, drink,
   And fresh from the farm in Ohio,
   The milk from the wagon will make you grow.

J. W. Beattie

Clink, clink, clinkety-clink,
The milkman's on his round I think.
Crunch, crunch come the milkman's feet,
Closer, closer along the street –
Clink, clink, clinkety-clink,
He's left our bottles of milk to drink.

C. Sausom

1. Oh, the milkman, busy milkman,
   He starts his day in the middle of the night;
   Oh, the milkman, busy milkman,
   He comes before it's light.
   He leaves a quart, or three or four,
   And Grade A milk for the baby next door.
   Oh, the milkman, busy milkman.

2. Oh, the milkman, cheery milkman,
   He makes his trip tho' the weather's cold or warm;
   Oh, the milkman, cheery milkman,
   He trudges thro' the storm.
   He brings us milk all fresh and cool.
   And leaves some here for the lunches at school,
   Oh, the milkman, cheery milkman.

See the postman dressed in blue,
He's walking, walking, walking, walking,
Do you think he'll bring to you
Some postcards and a letter too?

M. Norton

1. When the postman rings the doorbell
   And hands me the letters,
   I always hope to hear him saying:
   "And here's one for you."

2. Father, mother, sister, brother,
   They get all the letters,
   But some day I shall hear him saying:
   "And here's one for you."

Bring me a letter, postman.
Bring me a letter, do.
To-morrow at the garden gate
I will wait for you.

A. Todd

Come to the store with me,
Fast down the street.
We don't need a car,
We can go on our feet.
Daddy wants chervils
And apples and steak,
Mother wants bread
And strawberry cake.

1. I am going to market
   To buy a loaf of bread,
   But if the buns are shining ones
   I'll buy some buns instead.

2. I am going to market
   To buy a Cheddar cheese,
   And I shall tell the men who sell,
   A fresh one, if you please.

3. I am going to market
   To buy some juicy plums,
   The men will say 'They're fresh today'
   To everyone who comes.

4. I am going to market
   To see what I can see.
   I'll look around and spend a pound
   And come back home for tea.

E. J. Falconer

1. Good morning, Mister Grocerman,
   What do you have for me?
   Perhaps you brought me oranges,
   Perhaps a pound of tea.

2. What can be in those packages
   All neatly wrapped and tied?
   I'll help you, Mister Grocerman,
   I'll carry them inside.

N. Gillett

1. Spin, lassie, spin;
    The thread goes out and in;
    Growing as your tresses grow,
    Wisdom with each year will show;
    Spin, lassie, spin;
    Spin, lassie, spin.

2. Sing, lassie, sing;
    A merry heart to bring;
    While the golden flax you spin,
    Keep a cheerful heart within.
    Sing, lassie, sing;
    Sing, lassie, sing.

3. Learn, lassie, learn;
    Good fortune thus to earn;
    Learn to work and learn to play,
    Spinning on from day to day.
    Learn, lassie, learn;
    Learn, lassie, learn.

4. Smile, lassie, smile;
    And turn your wheel the while;
    As the thread of life you spin,
    Weave the smile and song therein;
    Smile, lassie, smile;
    Smile, lassie, smile.

Help me wind my ball of wool,
Hold it gently, do not pull.
Wind the wool and wind the wool,
Around, around, around.

1. See the shepherd leading
   His flocks to richest feeding.
   Thick and smooth the fleece must show,
   Then to shearing it will go.
   Wool to spin we're needing;
   The sheep graze on, unheeding.

2. See the spindles whirling,
   As each in place is twirling.
   From the wool the thread is spun,
   Then the weaving is begun.
   Wool to weave we're needing;
   The sheep graze on, unheeding.

3. Smooth the looms are plying,
   The shuttles swiftly flying.
   Yard by yard the cloth grows long,
   Woven of the thread so strong.
   Wool for cloth we're needing;
   The sheep graze on, unheeding.

J. Bassett

1. Down in a cottage lives Weaver John
   And a happy old John is he.
   Maud is the name of his dear old dame
   And a blessed old dame is she.

2. Whickity, whackity, click and clack,
   How the shuttles do dance and sing,
   Here they go, there they go, forth and back
   And a whackity song they sing.

From Ireland

I am the blacksmith!
Tools I forge and tools I make,
Spade and scythe and hoe and rake.
  Blow up the fire
  Flames are leaping higher!
Hammer and beat
Iron's white with heat!
  Kling, klang! Kling, klang!
The blacksmith's song we hear,
  Kling, klang! Kling, klang!
His song is true and clear.

I am the blacksmith!
Bring your stallion, bring your steed
I will shoe them to their need.
  Blow up the fire
  Flames are leaping higher!
High mounts the flame,
Children leave their game!
  Kling, klang! Kling, klang!
"Come on, come on," they say,
  Kling, klang! Kling, klang!
"The horse is shod today."

1. Blacksmith! Blacksmith!
    Blow, bellows, blow,
    Keep the coals a-burning,
    Glow, fire, glow.

2. Blacksmith! Blacksmith!
    Tink-tink-a-tank;
    Hammer on the anvil,
    Clink, clink, clank!

Blacksmith, Blacksmith, shoe my mare!
I want to go galloping off to the fair!
My little grey mare has cast a shoe –
Blacksmith, Blacksmith, hurry, do!

Steady, Master, take your time!
Fair won't start till the town bells chime.
Steady, slowly, hammer it truly,
Steady, slowly, hammer it surely.
Here's the nail and I hammer just there,
Nail goes straight if I hammer with care.
Now, young master, set off to the fair!

1. Ho, jolly blacksmith,
   Jolly, jolly blacksmith!
   Tell me whether you can shoe my horse;
   Kind and friendly,
   Very, very friendly,
   When you tie him, he will stand, of course.

2. Four lucky horse-shoes,
   Lucky, lucky horse-shoes!
   Pump your bellows till the cinders glow;
   Bang the anvil,
   Hammer on the anvil;
   Blacksmith music is the best I know.

Hit the nail a-right, Boys!
Hit it on the head,
Strike with all your might, Boys!
While the iron's red.

1. On the hill, where his black forge is glowing,
    Stands the blacksmith, the sparks round him blowing;
    Day by day, while the shadows are falling,
    Come the children to stand at his door;
    Like a bell clangs the great hammer calling,
    As it answers the loud bellows' roar.

2. With his bare, brawny arms freely swinging,
    Steady strokes on the wide anvil ringing,
    Like a shower rise the sparks round him pouring;
    How the strokes from the anvil rebound!
    While about him the bright flames are soaring
    Hill and dale with the echoes resound.

1. Saddle my pony free
    So it may carry me,
    Neighs like a trumpet blast,
    Runs like the wind so fast.
    Saddle my pony free
    So it may carry me.

2. Shoe then my pony well
    Front hooves and back as well,
    So it may carry me
    Over the land so free.
    Shoe then my pony well
    Front hooves and back as well.

3. Feed him then well each day
    Barley and oats and hay,
    Water so clear and bright,
    Straw for his bed at night.
    Feed him then well each day
    Barley and oats and hay.

All the night
And all day long
I hark to the sound
Of the blacksmith's song.

Red his fire –
The bright sparks fly
To dance with stars
In the joyous sky.

B. K. Pyke

1. Come, my little trowel, and my mortar thick,
   We must bind together all these brick, brick, brick.
   Pile them even, straight and true,
   Fill the chinks with mortar too.
   Come, my little trowel, smooth it quick, quick, quick!

2. See, my little trowel, how the pile grows tall!
   We must build it level or 'twill fall, fall, fall.
   Adding one and one and one
   Make a lot when you've begun.
   See, my little trowel, what a great, big wall!

A. Riley

"Pound, pound, pound,"
Says the little hammer.
Pound, pound, pound;
Pound the nails in tight.

"Saw, saw, saw,"
Says the little saw.
Saw, saw, saw;
Saw the board just right.

Can you be a carpenter,
At work the whole day long?
You will need so many tools,
Your arms must be quite strong.

First you saw and saw and saw,
Until the boards are cut!
Long ones, short ones, every size,
You need to build a hut.

1. Saw, saw, saw away,
   Saw the boards and saw the timbers,
   Saw, saw, saw away,
   We will build a house today.

2. Push, push, push the plane,
   See the curly shavings falling,
   Push, push, push the plane,
   Push with all your might and main.

3. Pound, pound, straight and true,
   Nails will hold the boards together,
   Pound, pound, straight and true,
   There is lots of work to do.

E. Bennett

The carpenter's hammer
Goes rap, rap, rap;
And his saw goes see, saw, see;
He hammers and hammers
And saws and saws
And builds a house for me.

1. Tailors are busily stitching away,
    Brown suits and ev'ry day blue ones.

2. Some are the suits that we wear when we play,
    Some are the nicest of new ones.

Needle bright,
Thread just right.
Fingers quick and nimble.
Stitches fine,
In a line,
And always wear a thimble.

Chimney Sweep, you black man,
You've a sooty shirt tonight.
All the washwomen from Paris
Can never wash it white.

From Switzerland

I sit at the city gate
Weaving baskets while you wait,
Baskets made of rush and reed,
Baskets made for every need.
A-tisket, a-tasket
I have an apple basket.

> *I have a bread basket.*
> *I have a pillow basket.*
> *etc., etc.*

48

Shoes for maiden and for wife,
　Boots for man and boy!
Shoemaking is the cobbler's life,
　Shoemaking is his joy.

> *"Come, bring your shoes, both worn and old,*
> *I'll make them new again!*
> *So get your shoes fresh heeled and soled,*
> *For next week it may rain!"*

Shoes to dance and shoes to play,
　Boots to keep out weather!
The cobbler's working all the day,
　Making shoes of leather.

> *"Come, bring your shoes, both worn and old,*
> *I'll make them new again!*
> *So get your shoes fresh heeled and soled,*
> *For next week it may rain!"*

1. With tap, tap, tap, from morn till night,
   He mends our shoes so strong and tight,
   He's always cheery, never weary,
   All day long.

2. He cuts the leather just to fit,
   He takes his thread and waxes it,
   Then in and out, to make it stout,
   He sews it strong.

3. Then tap, tap, tap, his hammer goes,
   And drives the pegs in even rows,
   When trim and neat and all complete,
   He sings a song.

There's a cobbler down our street,
Making shoes for father's feet,
With a knock-knock here
And a knock-knock there,
Knock-knock-knock and knock-knock-knock
His hammer goes till 5 o'clock.

(*Variations:* ... mending shoes for ...
　　　　　　　... mother's feet ...
　　　　　　　... little feet ...)

1.　There was a merry cobbler, busy as a bee,
　　Lily, lily, lily, lilylido.
　　When an old black crow came and perched upon a tree,
　　With his Qua! Qua! Qua! Qua!
　　Lily, lily, lily, lilylido.

2.　Now, wife, you go and drive yon pesky crow away,
　　Lily, lily, lily, lilylido.
　　Or he'll perch and croak till the ending of the day,
　　With his Qua! Qua! Qua! Qua!
　　Lily, lily, lily, lilylido.

3.　The cobbler's wife she tried to drive away the crow,
　　Lily, lily, lily, lilylido.
　　But the more she tried, why, the more he wouldn't go,
　　With his Qua! Qua! Qua! Qua!
　　Lily, lily, lily, lilylido.

4.　Then spoke the merry cobbler at the close of day,
　　Lily, lily, lily, lilylido.
　　If the crow won't go, we shall have to let him stay.
　　With his Qua! Qua! Qua! Qua!
　　Lily, lily, lily, lilylido.

D. Stephens

Sing a song of cobbler.
Jeremiah Cobbler
Mended boots and mended shoes
Go by one and go by twos.

Cobbler, cobbler, mend my shoe,
Have it done by half past two,
Stitch it up and stitch it down,
Make the strongest shoes in town.

Crooked heels and scruffy toes
Are all the kinds of shoes he knows.
He patches up the broken places,
Sews the seams and shines their faces.

I am a cobbler
And this is what I do:
Rap-tap-a-tap
To mend my shoe.

Guiseppi, the cobbler, makes my shoes,
He pounds them, rap, rap, rap!
He makes them small, he makes them big,
And ever he pounds, tap, tap, tap!

From Italy

THE WOOD GATHERER

Packet of twigs to kindle the fire,
   Will you buy two – for a sou!
Packets of twigs to kindle the fire,
I gather all day in hedge and in briar.
   Here's two – for a sou!

Over the trees the winds blow high,
   Will you buy two – for a sou!
Over the trees the winds blow high,
I pick up the twigs that scattered lie.
   Here's two – for a sou!

Blow on the leaves, your twigs will soon light,
   Will you buy two – for a sou!
Blow on the coals, your twigs will soon light,
Your pot will boil, your fire burns bright.
   Here's two – for a sou!

Fresh fish for sale, fresh fish for sale!
Be it trout or tunny whale!
Come and buy my nice, fresh fish!
Make yourself a tasty dish.
   Add garlic, spice,
   And serve with rice.

Fresh fish for sale, fresh fish for sale!
I have haddock, crab and snail,
And my salmon and my hake,
A most delicious chowder make.
   Add garlic, spice,
   And serve with rice.

The knife grinder twirls his wheel,
    Tira-loo!
And carefully whets the steel
    Tira-loo!
  Hear the call, up and down,
  "The knife grinder is in town!"
Bring your tools and bring your knife –
    Hurry, hurry, man and wife!

So bring your tools, straight and curved,
    Tira-loo!
Who comes first shall first be served,
    Tira-loo!
  Keep your tools sharp and bright –
  So your tasks are always light!
Bring your tools and bring your knife –
    Hurry, hurry, man and wife!

Today is the fair!
The pedlar is there!
His stall is piled high
With nice things to buy:
Pots, kettles and pans,
Pails, watering cans,
   And a pretty new toy
   For ev'ry girl and boy.

Stockings, shoes and socks,
Sweaters, coats and frocks,
Shawls for the old
To keep out the cold,
Pink bows for the hair
Of each maiden fair,
   And a pretty new toy
   For ev'ry girl and boy.

The market woman rides astride,
Her panniers swing from side to side,
Her donkey trots along the way.
"Giddap, Jeannot, 'tis market day!"
 Spinach, chard and lettuce too,
 Picked this morning wet with dew.
 Peas and cabbage, beans and kale,
 The market woman has for sale.

She rides her donkey through the gate,
The market clock is striking eight,
And in the square she builds her stall,
"Come and buy, good people all!"
 Spinach, chard and lettuce too,
 Picked this morning wet with dew.
 Peas and cabbage, beans and kale,
 The market woman has for sale.

The watchman wakes while people sleep.
He walks the road his watch to keep,
Then folk can sleep all through the night
And safely wake with morning light.
 Ding-dong-ding, the curfew bells now ring.
 Ding-dong-ding, so cover up your fire!
 Good night!

Who's at the gate? Is't friend or foe?
Answer now, the watchman must know.
Why do you want to pass the gate?
Curfew's rung, the hour is late.
 Ding-dong-ding, the curfew bells now ring.
 Ding-dong-ding, so cover up your fire!
 Good night!

Traveller man, traveller man,
In your yellow caravan,
Up and down the world you go
Tell me all the things you know.

Sun and moon and stars are bright,
Summer's green and winter's white,
And I'm a jolly traveller man
That rides inside a caravan.

The coachman cracks his whip
And tells the horse to go.
The horse he pulls with all his might
And stops when the coachman says whoa!

Ho-la, ho-la, ho-la, ho-la,
The world belongs to me;
A traveller lad whose life is glad,
I love whate'er I see.
Ho-la, ho-la, ho-la, ho-la,
My days are filled with joy,
And all the earth is sweet with mirth,
For me, a traveller boy.
Ah, how good just to be!
When the blue deeps of night
Bring their peace to the wood
Where we live with delight.
When the fire sings a tune
And the sweet voices ring,
In our hearts, then 'tis June
And the traveller lad is King!

M. F. Galvin

1. Down the hill the coach is coming,
   Who would like to drive today?
   Hark! The horn is sounding gay,
   Crack the whip and then away.

2. Now we dash along the highway,
   Over hill and thro' the glen;
   Rest the team awhile and then
   Crack the whip and off again.

Oh, I'm a jolly old cowboy,
Just off the Texas Plains;
My trade is cinching saddles,
And pulling bridle-reins.
I can throw the lassoo
With the greatest ease,
And mount my bronco pony,
And ride him when I please.

From Texas

THE DRUMMER MAN

A merry sound is in the air
'Tis the drummer with his fife!
So toss aside all work and care,
Lad and lassie, man and wife.
Rat-a-plan, plan, drummer man!
Fife shall blow, and drum shall roll!
Come, dance and farandole!

Brown buns to sell, brown buns to sell.
If I'd as much money as I could tell
I never would cry brown buns to sell.

Old chairs to mend, old chairs to mend.
If I'd as much money as I could spend
I never would cry old chairs to mend.

Cartwheels to turn, cartwheels to turn.
If I kept all the money which I could earn
I never would cry cartwheels to turn.

Fresh eggs for sale, fresh eggs for sale.
If I kept all the money in my pail
I never would cry fresh eggs to sell.

Fresh fish alive, fresh fish alive.
If for more money I need not strive
I never would cry fresh fish alive.

WORKING

The *farmer* is sowing his seed, in the field is sowing his seed.

The *reaper* is cutting the hay, in the meadow is cutting the hay.

The *gardener* is digging the ground, in the garden is digging the ground.

The *woodsman* is chopping the tree, in the forest is chopping the tree.

The *fisher* is drawing the nets, in the sea he is drawing the nets.

The *builder* is laying the bricks, in the wall is laying the bricks.

The *miller* is grinding the corn, in the mill he is grinding the corn.

The *baker* is kneading the dough, in the kitchen is kneading the dough.

The *mother* is rocking her child, in her arms she is rocking her child.

See Spring *page 50 for music.*

M. de Havas

This is the way we churn the cream,
Churn the cream, churn the cream,
This is the way we churn the cream
To make the yellow butter.
This is the way we dip the wick,
Dip the wick, dip the wick,
This is the way we dip the wick
And make a birthday candle.
or
. . . Christmas candle.

See the potter shape the clay,
Smoothing, patting, smoothing, patting,
At his table smoothing, patting,
Smoothing, patting shapes the clay.
Bowls and cups and little mugs,
Platters, pots and water jugs.
Plates for bread and plates for cakes
From his clay the potter makes!

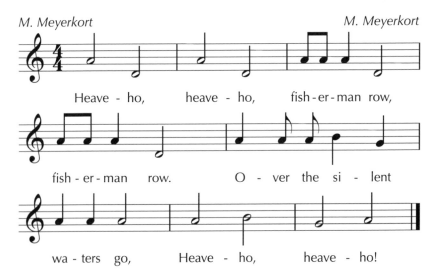

M. Meyerkort   M. Meyerkort

Heave - ho,   heave - ho,   fish - er - man row,

fish - er - man   row.   O - ver the si - lent

wa - ters go,   Heave - ho,   heave - ho!

Row, row, through the night,
Pull with all your might,
Far down the long river,
Row, row, through the night.

From China

Two little boats are on the sea,
All is calm as calm can be.
Gently the wind begins to blow,
Two little boats rock to and fro.
Loudly the wind begins to shout,
Two little boats are tossed about.
Gone is the wind, the storm, the rain,
Two little boats sail on again.

1. Boatman, sail away
   Over the sea;
   Boatman, sail away,
   Happy and free.

2. Boatman, speed away,
   Let your sail fill;
   Boatman, speed away,
   Go where you will.

Sailor, sailor, come ashore,
What have you brought for me?
Red coral, white coral,
Coral from the sea.

Sail, sail, pretty boat with me,
Sail, sail o'er the shining sea.
Out on the waves that dance and play,
Sail till the close of day.
Rock, rock, little boat with me,
Rock, rock on the stormy sea.
Out on the waves that toss and foam,
Rock till you bring me home.

Row to the fishing ground, row away.
How many fish have you caught today?
One for my father and one for my mother,
One for my sister and one for my brother,
One for you and another for me,
One for the fisher who went to sea.

From Denmark

Ferry me across the water.
Do, boatman, do.
If you've a penny in your purse
I'll ferry you.

I have a penny in my purse
And my eyes are blue.
So, ferry me across the water,
Do, boatman, do.

Step into my ferryboat,
Be they black or blue,
And for the penny in your purse
I'll ferry you.

C. Rossetti

The river is flowing,
The breezes are blowing,
The white sails are glowing for you and for me;
Let's go sailing,
Let's go sailing,
Sailing right down to the sea,
Go sailing right down to the sea.

Rocking and rolling the boat on the sea
Rocking and rolling with you and with me
Wind come and blow us so gently along
Mermaids come guide us and sing us a song.

The boatman he's a lucky man!
No one can do as the boatman can;
He can dance and he can sing,
The boatman is up to everything!
Hi-o, away we go
Floating down the river on the O-hi-o!

From America

In my bark canoe where waters blue,
Flowing gently there, I paddle through,
The waters blue in my canoe.

An Ojibway Song

1. Sail, fishing boat, sail, fishing boat,
   Out of the harbour into waters deep,
   Trailing your nets, trailing your nets,
   Fishing for food while other people sleep.

2. Sail, fishing boat, sail, fishing boat,
   Into the harbour from the waters blue,
   Laden with fish, silvery fish,
   Food for the people who depend on you.

L. M. Fox

1. Oh hur-a-lo! The tides do flow,
   That bring the good fishing to me;
   And forth go I
   My luck for to try
   By casting my net in the sea.
   My net in the sea,
   Where the big fishes be,
   More pow'r to the pull of my arm:
   And e'er so long as the fishes can swim,
   No fishermen fear for harm.

2. Oh hur-a-lo! The tides do flow,
   And I must sail out on the sea;
   But I'll be back
   With net like a pack,
   All heavy with fishes for thee.
   With fishes for thee,
   And for thee and for me,
   And wife thou shalt broil them warm;
   And e'er so long as fishes can swim,
   No fishermen fear for harm.

From Cornwall

Here we go round the mul - ber - ry bush, the

mul - ber - ry bush, the mul - ber - ry bush.

Here we go round the mul - ber - ry bush on a

or: so

cold and frost - y morn - ing.
ear - ly in the morn - ing.

2. This is the way we wash our hands . . .
3. This is the way we clean our teeth . . .
4. This is the way we brush our hair . . .

Suggested directions: *The children walk around freely in an open circle formation. In the subsequent verses they mime the activities named including as many actions.*

For the child aged 3: Actions concerning the care of the physical body.

For the child aged 4: Actions concerning the care of the home and house.

For the child aged 5: Activities of artisans and related professions.

The earth is firm beneath my feet,
The sun shines bright above
And here stand I so straight and strong,
All things to know and love.

I can turn myself and turn myself
Or curl up when I will,
I can stand on tiptoe reaching high,
Or hold myself quite still.

M. de Havas

Big feet,
Black feet.
Going up and down the street;
Dull and shiny
Father's feet,
Walk by me!

Nice feet,
Brown feet,
Going up and down the street;
Pretty, dainty,
Ladies' feet,
Trip by me!

Small feet,
Light feet,
Going up and down the street;
Little children's
Happy feet,
Run by me!

I. Thompson

Good morning, you trotters!
What are your names?
I am called Jumper,
I am called Stumper.
This foot's name is Scallywag
And this foot's name is Raggletag,
And Scallywag and Raggletag
Are going on a journey.
They journey through the grass and dew
And both get soaking through and through.
They journey over stones and rocks,
Their feet become like heavy blocks.
They creep upstairs to bed at night,
And shut their little door quite tight.

From Germany

Ring-a-ring o'roses
A pocket full of posies
A tishoo, a tishoo,
We all bow down.

The king has sent his daughter
To fetch a pail of water
A tishoo, a tishoo,
We all kneel down.

The robin on the steeple
Is singing to the people
A tishoo, a tishoo,
We all fall down.

Picking up the daisies,
Picking up the daisies
A tishoo, a tishoo,
We all stand up again.

O. Carrington

Stepping over stepping stones, one, two, three,
Stepping over stepping stones, come with me!
The river's very fast,
And the river's very wide,
And we'll step across on stepping stones
And reach the other side.

1. Behold the giant big and strong:
   From hill to hill I stride along.
   As over rock and stream I go,
   I sing fa-rol-dee dandy-O!

2. Behold the dwarf inside the hill:
   My tiny hammer's never still.
   I sing and work deep under ground,
   And as I tap, the rocks resound.

                    J. Mehta

Clipperty clop goes my little pony,
Galloping over the roadway stony.
On we go, up we go, then we go down,
Galloping gaily into town.

Clipperty clop we ride home together,
We never worry about the weather,
Whether it's sunny or whether it's not
Back we ride gaily, trot, trot, trot.

My white horses like to step peaceful and slow
Over mountains, through valleys so upright they go.
My brown horses merrily trot in the sun
With their silver hooves beating the ground as they run.
My black horses gallop with courage around
And they throw up their heads as they hammer the ground.

From Germany

Go, my pony, go,
King Sun begins to glow.
We're riding into spring –
Then ring, oh bluebell, ring.
Trot, my pony trot,
The sun grows big and hot.
We're riding into a summer's day
All wreathed with roses red and gay.
Gallop, pony gallop on,
Hey dee hop, the summer's gone.
We're riding into autumn now,
The leaves are falling from the bough.
Stop, my pony whoa,
The cold brings frost and snow.
Winter's not the time to ride;
Roads are icy far and wide.

From Germany

Roly-poly, roly-poly,
Tight and tighter gets the ball.
Comes the kitten with her mitten
One, two, three unrolls it all.

1. Hand in hand, you see us well
   Creep like a snail into his shell.
     Ever nearer, ever nearer,
     Ever closer, ever closer.
   Very snug indeed you dwell
   Snail within your tiny shell.

2. Hand in hand you see us well
   Creep like a snail out of his shell.
     Ever further, ever further,
     Ever wider, ever wider.
   Who'd have thought this tiny shell
   Could have held us all so well.

Oh how slowly, oh how slowly,
Comes the snail along his track.
Seven days he takes to travel
Just a little way and back.
Oh how slowly, oh how slowly,
Through the grass he makes his trail –
Gracious! I would run much faster
If I were a little snail.

From Germany

We'll make a little journey
To the curly house of snail.
Round we go until we find him
Hidden in his coat of mail.
Then we turn and go back homeward
Still a-winding all the way,
Till we come out of the tunnel
To the sunny light of day.

M. Bucknall

68

FINGER GAMES

Pages 69 to 73

I have built a little nest – look inside, look inside,
Hungry birdies with their beaks open wide, open wide,
And the little birdies grow – day by day, day by day,
Till they spread their wings and fly – far away, far away.

My mother and your mother
Went over the way,
Said my mother to your mother,
"It's chop-a-nose day."
    (Waggle tip of baby's nose)

Here sits the Lord Mayor,
    (Touch forehead with fist)

Here sit his two men,
    (Point to eyes with forefingers)

Here sits the cock,
    (Point to right cheek)

Here sits the hen,
    (Point to left cheek)

Here sit the little chickens,
    (Point to tip of nose)

Here they run in,
    (Point into mouth)

Chinchopper, Chinchopper,
    (Chuck the chin)

Chinchopper, Chin!

1. Deep the cellar, timbers high,
   (Both hands point down, then up — arms full length)

2. Pointed roof against the sky,
   (Bring finger tips together over the head)

3. Drive the nails in straight and true,
   (Hammer with one fist on the other)

4. Build a house for me and you.
   (Continue to hammer)

5. Windows, shining eyes to see,
   (Circle hands at eyes)

6. Doors that open to welcome me,
   (Gesture of opening wide the arms)

7. Fire upon the hearth stone bright,
   (Close arms around self as though hugging self snug and warm)

8. That is HOME on winter's night.
   (Continue as 7)

                                      A. Riley

Build the house up, build so high,
Point the chimney to the sky.
See the roof and see the floor,
See the pretty yellow door.

Here the mother makes the bread,
Here the baby goes to bed,
Here the little children play,
Dancing through the happy day.

Knock at the knocker,
  (Tap the forehead with fist)

Pull down the bell,
  (Gently pull ear-lobe)

Peep through the keyhole,
  (Screw up one eye and peep with other)

Lift the latch,
  (Gently push up tip of nose)

Walk in and
  (Open mouth and point with finger)

Take a chair.
  (Tickle under chin)

These birds are very sleepy,
These birds are tired today.
Tomorrow they will spread their wings
And flutter right away.

Here are ten merry men,
  (The fingers)

See how they dance and play:
  (Move the fingers)

Two stand straight,
  (Forefingers)

Two join hands,
  (Thumbs)

The rest they run away.
  (Tuck away rest of fingers)

I have ten little fingers, they all belong to me,
I can make them do things, do you want to see?
I can open them up wide, I can shut them up tight;
I can put them together, I can put them out of sight;
I can put them way up high, I can put them way down low;
I can fold them together and sit just so.

Here is the deep blue sea,
This is the boat and this is me.
All the bright fishes down below
Waggle their tails, and off they go.

I can make a snowman,
I can build him high.
I can make a snowman
Reaching to the sky.

We can make two snowmen,
We can build them high.
We can build two snowmen
Reaching to the sky.

We can make three
               four
               five, etc.

During Verse 1 a child pretends to build a snowman. He puts one fist on the ground and pretends to build up, fist upon fist, until he is stretching up as high as he can.
During Verse 2, two children perform these movements.
During Verse 3 there are three children . . . And so on.

Here is a tree with its leaves so green.
    (Arms *outstretched*)

Here are the apples that hang between.
    (Clenched fists)

When the wind blows, the apples will fall.
    (Drop arms)

Here is a basket to gather them all.
    (Fingers interlocking)

I'm going to build a little house,
With windows big and bright.
With chimney tall and curling smoke,
Drifting out of sight.
In winter when the snowflakes fall,
Or when I hear a storm,
I'll go sit in my little house,
Where I'll be snug and warm.

I saw a little fish in the pond,
Wherever has he gone?
He disappeared so quickly,
I wonder what was wrong.
He might have heard his mother call
And so he went away.
Please, little fish, come up again,
I want to see you. Stay!

                    I. Tupaj

From Germany   *J. Knierim*

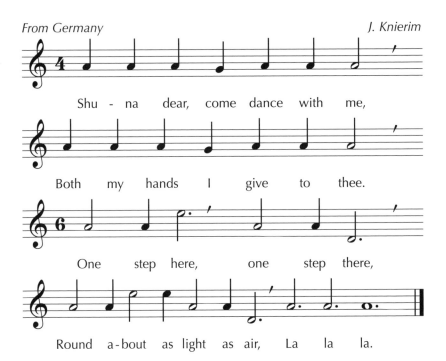

Shu - na   dear,   come   dance   with   me,

Both   my   hands   I   give   to   thee.

One   step   here,   one   step   there,

Round   a-bout   as light   as   air,   La   la   la.

2. With my hands I clap, clap, clap.
   With my feet I tap, tap, tap.
   One step here, one step there,
   Round about as light as air,
   La la la.

3. With my finger tick, tick, tick.
   With my head I nick, nick, nick.
   One step here, one step there,
   Round about as light as air,
   La la la.

Traditional   J. Aulie

Here is the church, here is the stee - ple.

O - pen the doors and see all the peo - ple.

Here is the par - son climb-ing the stairs,

Here he is say - ing his prayers.

Traditional   P. Patterson

There were two crows sat on a stone, fal - de -

ral, fal - de - ral, fal - de - ral.

2. One flew away and then there was one, fal-de-ral . . ..

3. The other seeing his neighbour gone, fal-de-ral . . ..

4. He flew away and then there were none, fal-de-ral . . ..

Traditional   J. Hughes

Dance   Thumb - kin   dance;   Now

dance ye   mer - ry - men,   ev' - ry - one.   For

Thumb - kin   he   can   dance   a - lone;

Thumb - kin   he   can   dance   a - lone.

Dance   Ma - ry   Tos - sle dance;   Now

dance ye   mer - ry - men,   ev' - ry - one.   For

Ma - ry   she   can   dance   a - lone;   Ma - ry

Continued...

Tos - sle she can dance a - lone.

Dance Rue Whis - tle dance; Now

dance ye mer - ry - men, ev' - ry - one. For

Rue Whis - tle he can dance a - lone;

Rue Whis - tle he can dance a - lone.

Dance Pen - ny Rue dance; Now

dance ye mer - ry - men, ev' - ry - one. For

Continued...

Pen - ny Rue she can dance a - lone;

Pen - ny Rue she can dance a - lone.

Dance lit - tle Pen - ny dance; Now

dance ye mer - ry - men, ev' - ry - one. But

lit - tle Pen - ny can not dance a - lone, So

we can dance to - ge - ther home; So

we can dance to - ge - ther home.

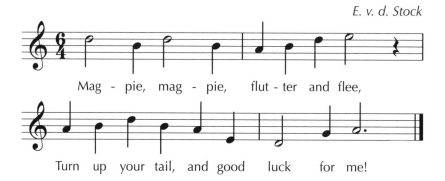

E. v. d. Stock

Mag - pie, mag - pie, flut - ter and flee,

Turn up your tail, and good luck for me!

Traditional   *J. Aulie*

Cush-y cow, bon-ny, let down thy milk, And

I will give thee a gown of silk, A

gown of silk and a sil - ver tee, If

thou wilt let down thy milk for me.

Traditional   J. Aulie

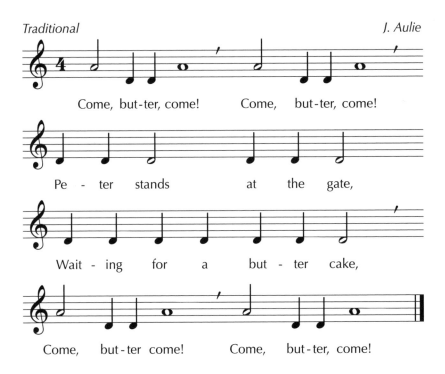

Come, but-ter, come!   Come,   but-ter, come!

Pe - ter   stands   at   the   gate,

Wait - ing   for   a   but - ter   cake,

Come,   but-ter come!   Come,   but-ter, come!

Westminster chime
Up in the tow'r,
Telling the time
Each quarter hour.

Traditional

J. Aulie

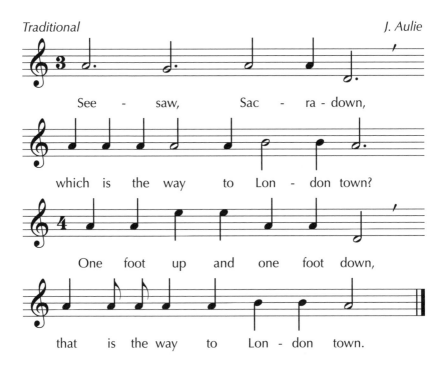

See - saw, Sac - ra - down,

which is the way to Lon - don town?

One foot up and one foot down,

that is the way to Lon - don town.

1. Susy, little Susy, now what is the news?
   The geese are going barefoot because they've no shoes.
   The cobbler has leather, but no last has he,
   So he cannot make them the shoes, don't you see?

2. Susy, little Susy, some pennies I pray,
   To buy a little supper of sugar and whey.
   I'll sell my nice bed and go sleep on the straw,
   Feathers will not tickle and mice will not gnaw.

From Germany

Traditional   J. Aulie

Baa, baa, black sheep, have you an-y wool?

Yes, sir, yes, sir, three bags full.

One for the mas-ter and one for the dame, And

one for the lit-tle boy who lives down the lane.

1. There sat a little girl upon a sunny hill
   And a bird upon the tree tira-lila-lil.

2. Then said the little girl as she sat upon the hill
   In winter you will find it is chilly-chilly-chil.

3. I've a pretty little house up yonder on the hill
   Where you can live with me if you willy-willy-will.

From Norway

82

Traditional   J. Aulie

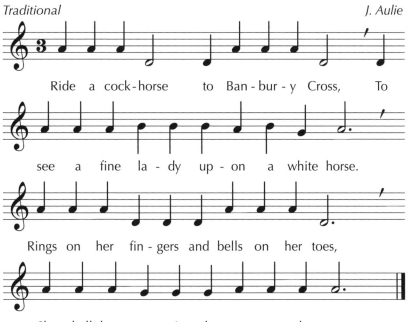

Ride a cock-horse   to Ban - bur - y Cross,   To

see   a   fine   la - dy   up - on   a   white horse.

Rings on   her   fin - gers and bells   on   her toes,

She shall have mu - sic wher - ev - er   she goes.

Five tiny fairies hiding in a flower.
Five tiny fairies caught in a shower.
Daddy Cock-a-doodle standing on one leg.
Old Mother Speckle-top lays a golden egg.
Old Mrs. Crosspatch comes with her stick.
Fly away fairies quick, quick, quick.

Traditional   J. Aulie

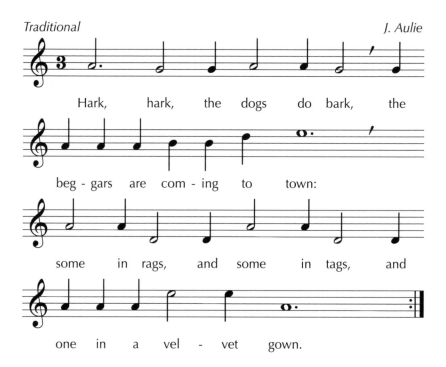

Hark, hark, the dogs do bark, the

beg - gars are com - ing to town:

some in rags, and some in tags, and

one in a vel - vet gown.

1. Now once there was a shepherd
   Who did not care for sheep.
   He was a lazy fellow
   And always fell asleep.

2. One day the wolf came running
   And took away a sheep.
   Up woke the lazy fellow,
   Gone were sheep and sleep.

From Germany

Traditional   E. v. d. Stock

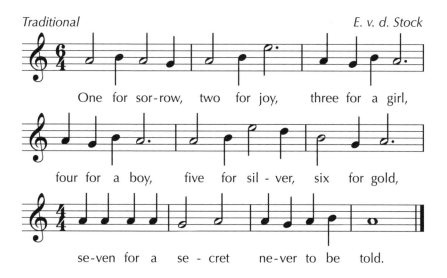

One for sor-row, two for joy, three for a girl,

four for a boy, five for sil - ver, six for gold,

se-ven for a se - cret ne-ver to be told.

Traditional   K. Klaveness

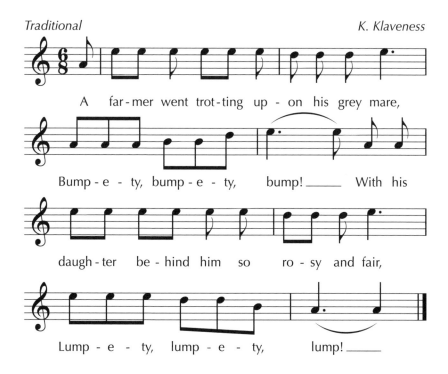

A far-mer went trot-ting up - on his grey mare,

Bump - e - ty, bump - e - ty, bump! _____ With his

daugh - ter be - hind him so ro - sy and fair,

Lump - e - ty, lump - e - ty, lump! _____

Traditional

J. Aulie

There was an old wo-man tossed up in a bas-ket,

Se-ven-teen times as high as the moon. And

where she was go-ing I could not but ask it,

For in her hand she car-ried a broom. "Old

wo-man, old wo-man, old wo-man," quoth I, "O

whi-ther, O whi-ther, O whi-ther so high?" "To

sweep the cob - webs out of the sky."

"May I go with thee?" "Yes, by and by."

Traditional   *C. A. Lindenberg*

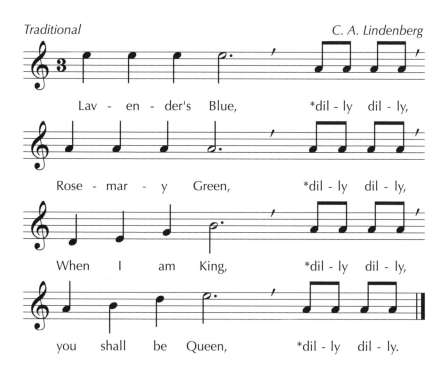

Lav - en - der's Blue,   *dil - ly dil - ly,

Rose - mar - y Green,   *dil - ly dil - ly,

When   I   am   King,   *dil - ly dil - ly,

you   shall   be   Queen,   *dil - ly dil - ly.

dilly dilly on any of these Pentatonic notes:

1   2   3   4   5   6   7

and modulate freely:

Traditional   *C. A. Lindenberg*

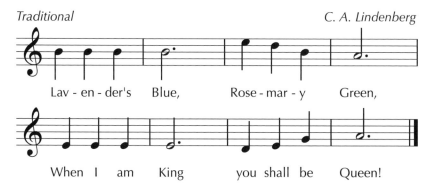

Lav - en - der's   Blue,   Rose - mar - y   Green,

When   I   am   King   you shall be   Queen!

Traditional   J. Aulie

One mist - y moist - y morn - ing, When

cloud - y was the wea - ther, I

chanced to meet an old man,

Cloth - éd all in lea - ther,

Cloth - éd all in lea - ther with a

strap be - neath his chin.

"How do you do?" "How do you do?"

"How do you do?" a - gain.

1. I will build you a house
    If you do not cry,
    A house, little girl,
    As tall as the sky.

2. I will build you a house
    Of golden dates
    The freshest of all
    For the steps and the gates.

3. I will furnish the house
    For you and for me
    With walnuts and hazels
    Fresh from the tree.

4. I will build you a house
    And when it is done
    I will roof it with grapes
    To keep out the sun.

From Arabia

On the Bibblibonty hill
Stands a Bibblibonty house.
In the Bibblibonty house
Are Bibblibonty people.
The Bibblibonty people
Have Bibblibonty children.
And the Bibblibonty children
Take a Bibblibonty sup
With a Bibblibonty spoon
From a Bibblibonty cup.

From Holland

P. Patterson
P. Patterson

Ro - cky, ro - cky - roo,

Off we go with you.

O - ver the fields a - way we go,

Ro - cky - rock on a ned - de - ly - no.

Ro - cky, ro - cky - roo,

Off we go with you.

2. Off they go with me, rock a neddely-nee,
   Over the hills away we go,
   Through the frost and icy snow.
   Rocky, rocky-ree, off they go with me.

Continued...

3. Rocky, rocky-roo, off we go with you,
   Over the fields away we go,
   Grass and flowers wherever we go.
   Rocky, rocky-roo, off we go with you.

4. Rocky, rocky-ree, off you come with me,
   Over the land and over the sea,
   Rocky-rock on a neddely-nee.
   Rocky, rocky-ree, off you come with me.

Little robin redbreast
Sat up a tree.
Up went pussy-cat
And down went he.

Down came pussy-cat
And away robin ran.
Says robin redbreast:
Catch me if you can!

Little robin redbreast
Hopped upon a wall.
Pussy-cat jumps after him
And nearly got a fall.

Little robin chirped and sang
And what did pussy say?
Pussy-cat, he said miaow!
And robin hopped away!

Traditional

Traditional

N. Foster

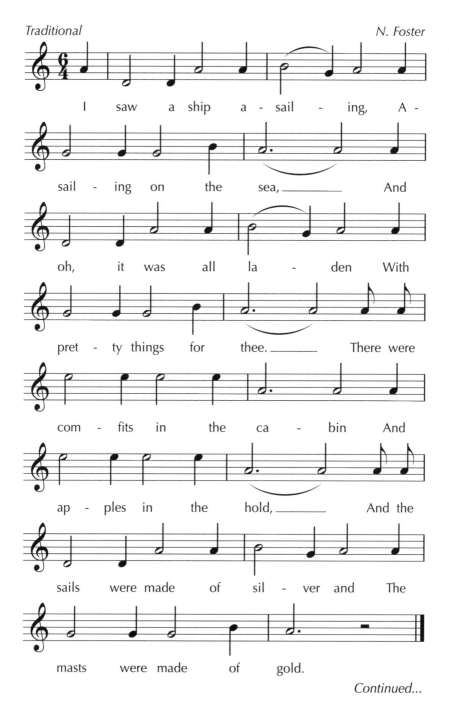

I saw a ship a-sail-ing, A-
sail-ing on the sea, _____ And
oh, it was all la - den With
pret - ty things for thee. _____ There were
com - fits in the ca - bin And
ap - ples in the hold, _____ And the
sails were made of sil - ver and The
masts were made of gold.

Continued...

2. The four and twenty sailors
   That stood between the decks,
   Were four and twenty white mice
   With chains around their necks;
   The captain was a little duck
   With a packet on this back,
   And when the ship began to move
   The captain cried "Quack, quack!'

1. Oh, when I was a shepherd,
   So very small indeed,
   They sent me up the mountain,
   My nimble lambs to feed,
   There came a wolf to dine
   And ate my fattest three,
   "My old grey glutton fine,
   Please, save a skin for me!"

2. Oh, when I was a shepherd,
   So very, very small,
   At night my sheep I folded
   So I could count them all.
   "Oh, skip, my nimble lambs
   And get you all to bed,
   Your fleecy wool is safe,
   The old grey wolf is dead!"

   From France

Mary had a silver spoon,
Mary had a gay balloon,
Mary slept beneath the sun,
The day that she was one.

Mary had a golden bell,
Mary had a doll as well,
Mary had a bonnet blue,
The day that she was two.

Mary had a silken shawl,
Mary had a bouncing ball,
Mary threw the ball to me,
The day that she was three.

Mary had a teddy bear,
Mary had new shoes to wear,
Painted red her bedroom door,
The day that she was four.

A little rabbit on a hill
Was jumping up and down.
His fluffy tail was round and white,
His pointed ears were brown.

But when he heard a tiny sound
His eyes turned black as coal,
His little whiskers trembled, and
He scuttled down his hole.

ELEPHANT

Right foot, left foot, see me go.
I am grey and big and slow.
I come walking down the street
With my trunk and four big feet.

Jump, jump, jump,
Goes the kangaroo.
I thought there was one,
But I see there are two.
The mother takes her young one
Along in a pouch,
Where he can nap like a child
On a couch.
Jump, jump, jump.

J. Aulie

Mouse, wee mouse, — where's your house, —
Mous - ey - kin — are you in? —

Un - der - neath the floor, be -
Yes, here's mous - ey speak - ing,

side the kitch - en door, is
can't you hear me squeak - ing?

that your house, mouse wee mouse?
Squeak, squeak, squeak, squeak, squeak, squeak.

1. A little mouse
    Went to a house
    To find some cheese for tea.
    He made a hole
    And in he stole
    But oh! What did he see?
    A cheese upon the table sat,
    Beside it purred a pussy cat
    As pleasant as could be.
    The little mouse made haste to go
    He said, "With pussy sitting so
    There is no room for me!"

2. The little mouse went next to find
    A tiny piece of bacon rind,
    To carry home for tea.
    A dog beside the bacon sat,
    He looked so very large and fat
    The mouse made haste to flee.
    The little mouse
    Began to grouse,
    It's very plain to see:
    No bacon rind,
    No cheese I find
    But just dry bread for tea.

Auntie Lucy
Sat on a goosey.
Whoop, said the goosey –
Away flew Aunt Lucy.

From Holland

96

Valentines, valentines, red, white and blue.
I'll find a nice one and give it to you.

Five little valentines were having a race.
The first little valentine was frilly with lace.
The second little valentine had a funny face.
The third little valentine said, "I love you."
The fourth little valentine said, "I do, too."
The fifth little valentine was sly as a fox.
He ran the fastest to your valentine box.

Flowers are sweet, this is true,
But for my valentine I'll choose you.

Mrs. Kitty, nice and fat,
With her kittens four,
Went to sleep upon the mat,
Beside the kitchen door.
Mrs. Kitty heard a noise,
And up she jumped in glee.
"Kittens, maybe that's a mouse!
Let us go and see."
Creeping, creeping, creeping on,
Silently they stole.
Back the little mouse had gone,
Back into its hole.

1. My donkey, my dear,
    Had a pain in his head.
    A kind lady gave him
    A bonnet of red,
    And little shoes of lavender
    Lav-lav-lavender
    To keep him from the cold.

2. My donkey, my dear,
    Had a pain in his throat.
    A kind lady gave him
    A button-up coat,
    And little shoes of lavender
    Lav-lav-lavender
    To keep him from the cold.

3. My donkey, my dear,
    Had a pain in his chest.
    A kind lady gave him
    A thick woolly vest,
    And little shoes of lavender
    Lav-lav-lavender
    To keep him from the cold.

From France

This little mule wants corn,
This little mule wants hay.
Give them all that they can eat,
And let them munch away.

1. There was a little man and his name was Grice,
   He built himself a little house right on the ice.
   Then he wished he had a hen,
   Chip-chip is my hen,
   Evenings in the little cage,
   Mornings in the pen.

2. Then he wished he had a sheep.,
   Trip-trap is my sheep,
   Chip-chip is my hen,
   Evenings in the little cage,
   Mornings in the pen.

3. Then he wished he had a cow.
   Nonny-gow is my cow,
   Trip-trap is my sheep,
   Chip-chip is my hen,
   Evenings in the little cage,
   Mornings in the pen.

4. Then he wished he had a calf.
   Duck-dalf is my calf,
   Nonny-gow is my cow,
   Trip-trap is my sheep,
   Chip-chip is my hen,
   Evenings in the little cage,
   Mornings in the pen.

From Holland

1. The rooster in our farmyard is crowing off his head;
    And Father's shouting loudly, he's fallen out of bed.
    And Betty, in the kitchen, is far from feeling glad
    Because the cat has tripped her up, and that has made her mad!
    Outside a great confusion, and horns begin to blow,
    What's wrong! 'Tis Nancy's wedding-morn,
            That's all, and now you know.

2. The chickens in our hen-run are clucking fit to burst;
    The noisy dogs are barking, but Father's still the worst.
    He's storming round the parlour and ev'ry one knows why:
    For Mother's busy fixing up his brand new wedding tie.
    The farm is like a mad-house, with bellow, bark and crow,
    What's wrong! 'Tis Nancy's wedding morn,
            That's all, and now you know.

3. And now the chaise is coming, I hear the horses' feet,
    And Father's so excited he's fallen off the seat.
    Then comes an awful clatter when Betty drops a pail,
    Because she's fallen down again on our old Tabby's tail!
    The lads out on the roadway are shouting "Time to go!"
    What's wrong! 'Tis Nancy's wedding morn,
            That's all, and now you know.

4. Now ev'rybody's shouting, but no one heeds the call;
    The din grows loud, but Father is loudest of them all.
    And Betty's burnt her fingers, and Mother's torn her dress,
    And ev'ry body, in and out, is crazy, more or less!
    But now, at last they're starting, it is a sight to see!
    What's wrong? 'Tis Nancy's wedding-morn,
            And that's enough for me!

From Wales

1. I've got a mule, her name is Sal,
   Fifteen miles on the Erie Canal.
   She's a good old worker and a good old pal,
   Fifteen miles on the Erie Canal.
   We've hauled some barges in our day,
   Filled with lumber, coal and hay,
   And we know ev'ry inch of the way
   From Albany to Buffalo.
   Low bridge, ev'ry body down!
   Low bridge, for we're going thro' a town,
   And you'll always know your neighbour,
   You'll always know your pal,
   If you ever navigated on the Erie Canal.

2. We better get along our way,
   Fifteen miles on the Erie Canal.
   'Cause you bet your life I'd never part with Sal,
   Fifteen miles on the Erie Canal.
   Git up there, mule, here comes a lock,
   We'll make Rome 'bout six o' clock,
   One more trip and back we'll go
   Right back home to Buffalo.
   Low bridge, ev'ry body down!
   Low bridge, for we're going thro' a town,
   And you'll always know your neighbour,
   You'll always know your pal,
   If you ever navigated on the Erie Canal.

From America

Sunday Bread

In the town lives the baker. On Saturday he wants to bake the bread for Sunday. He takes a bowl and from his sack pours flour into it, and then he adds milk. He kneads it and leaves it on the table to rise. Then he goes into the garden to have a rest. He lies down under a tree and soon dreams his sweet baker's dream.

The dough in the bowl rises, and rises over the edge and looks around and says: "Oh, how large the world is. I want to rise more and see the wide world:

> I rise and rise, higher and high,
> I rise and rise to see the sky."

And the dough rises up the chimney, and to the top of the chimney and there he sings:

> "I rise and rise, higher and high,
> I rise and rise to see the sky."

The song awakens the baker, he looks up, sees the dough on the chimney and says: "What are you doing up there?" – "I want to see the wide world," says the dough. – "Well, I will help you to see the wide world. Come down."

The dough comes down and goes back into the bowl. Then the baker takes the dough, adds raisins and nuts and divides the mixture into pieces. He rolls each piece out and kneads it and kneads it.

He puts the loaves on the baking-tray and pushes them into the oven. When they are baked goldy-brown and crisp he lays them into his basket and goes into the street, where he calls out:

> "Sunday bread, Sunday bread,
> Baked with nuts and raisins red."

Doors open and children come running along and say: "A Sunday loaf, please." – "Yes, here you are," says the baker. – "A Sunday loaf, please." - "Yes," says the baker and shares out the loaves of bread. The children say: "Thank you," and skip away.

Then the baker looks into his basket and says: "And now my dough HAS gone into the wide world." And he goes home.

A. Vinnal

Grusha

Little Grusha had no dolls. She took straw and bunched it and tied it to make a doll whom she called Masha. Then Grusha picked up her doll, Masha, and rocked her in her arms and sang to her:

"Hushabye, hushabye, sleep,
Masha, my baby, sleep."

L. Tolstoy

Grandmother

Once upon a time a grandmother lived with her granddaughter. When the granddaughter was very young she slept all day long. Her grandmother baked bread and cleaned the house. She washed their clothes and sewed. She spun wool and wove it into warm garments for her granddaughter.

Many years later grandmother had grown old. She could no longer work for them. She sat by the fire and dozed most of the day. Now her granddaughter baked bread, washed, spun, sewed and wove for her grandmother.

L. Tolstoy

Grandfather

An old man planted a number of little apple trees. People laughed at him and said:

"What is the good of planting all these trees? It will be many years before they bear fruit and you will no longer be alive to eat any of it when they do bear fruit." The old man answered:

"I shall not be alive to eat the fruit, but when other people eat apples from these trees they will be grateful to me for planting them."

L. Tolstoy

Varya

Varya had a green finch. She kept it shut up in a cage. It never once sang. So Varya asked her green finch:

"Why do you not sing?" The little bird answered:

"Let me go free. Then I shall sing again all day long."

L. Tolstoy

Roska

Roska had given birth to a litter of puppies. They lay on a bed of straw in a corner of the yard. One day, when she went out to hunt for food, the farmer's children found the puppies and took them into the farm house. They laid them on the broad, flat top of the brick stove to keep warm.

When Roska came back and found her puppies gone she searched everywhere for them. First she barked, then she howled. In the end she found them and stood whining in front of the stove because she could not reach her puppies.

So the children lifted down her puppies and gave them back to Roska. Roska picked each one up carefully in her mouth, then carried them back one by one to their bed in the straw.

L. Tolstoy

Katya

Very early one morning Katya set out for the woods to look for mushrooms. She took Masha with her. Masha was very young.

On their way to the woods they had to cross a stream. Katya took off her shoes and stockings, lifted Masha up pick-a-back and waded out into the stream.

"Do not wriggle, Masha," she said, "and do not squeeze my neck too tightly with your little arms or I shall not be able to breathe." So Katya and Masha got safely across the stream.

L. Tolstoy

The *following five stories are accounts of actual happenings. Collected by M. Bucknall.*

The Boy and the Butterfly

Once Paul was playing on the sands when a coloured butterfly flew down just in front of him. The butterfly stayed quietly until Paul reached her. And then he gently cupped her in his hands.

After a while she flew off and settled down on the sands a little further away.

Again Paul went after the butterfly. She folded her wings and stayed in his hands. "Butterfly, don't fly away. Stay with me," he said. The butterfly answered:

"You may catch me once again and then I must fly away to my friends, the thistles."

Again the butterfly opened her wings and fluttered away settling on the sand until Paul had reached her. Gently he picked her up and so they stayed a long time gazing at each other. Then he opened his hands wide and she fluttered away on the breeze while Paul watched until he could see her no more.

The Boy and the Ants

Once there was a boy called Christopher. He had many pot plants growing on his window sill in the sunlight. Everyday he watered them and watched them grow and unfold their green shoots. One day he saw that they were covered with ants, busily hurrying and scurrying up and down every stalk.

"What can I do to get rid of the ants?" he wondered. "Shall I pour hot water over them and destroy them?" Christopher did not want to do that. He thought of another way to try. "I will talk to the ants," he said.

So he took a stool and sat down in front of the ants and began to speak to them: "You have come into my room without asking me," he said. "You are not in the right place. The garden is your home. Go back, little ants, to the place where you belong. Enjoy the earth, the plants and the sun and leave my room in peace. I will give you three days to leave my plants." Christopher left the window open and invited the ants to go down into the garden.

On the next day some of the ants had already gone. Christopher sat down on his stool and again he spoke to the ants: "You are not in the right place," he said, "go back into the garden where you belong. Enjoy the earth and the plants and the sun and leave my room in peace."

On the third day there were only a few scout ants left, trying to find their way out. "Thank you little ants," said Christopher, "Goodbye."

Mice

In a cottage there once lived two old ladies. Around the cottage was a large orchard of apple trees. Every year the old ladies sold the apples, and made jam and pureé and chutney which they sold at the market. That was how they earned their living.

One year many field mice came to the orchard. They nibbled at every apple which fell to the ground. The old ladies saw the nibbled apples lying in the grass.

"No one will buy apples with holes in them," said one old lady to the other.

"No, they will not," said the other old lady, "but I know what to do." She collected all the bruised and nibbled apples and put them in a box. She stood beside the box and she talked to the field mice.

"This is your box of apples," she said, "you can eat as much as you like from it. But please leave the good apples for us. My sister and I must sell them to earn a living."

From then onwards the two old ladies had no more trouble. But they always made sure that the box of bruised apples was kept full for the field-mice.

Moles

In a cottage in the country there lived an old couple. The old man was a keen gardener and in the middle of the garden was a beautiful green lawn which was his pride and joy. One day moles came to the garden. Soon the velvet smooth grass was covered with brown earth mounds which the moles threw up as they dug their tunnels under the ground. The old man was sad to see how they had spoiled the green lawn which he had tended with such love and care.

One morning he got up early, just as the sun was rising, and went into the garden. He talked very quietly to the moles: "The cows in the meadow next door will not mind your digging and your little mounds of earth. Please would you leave our garden and go to live next door?"

Then he began to level out the molehills and to rake the lawn smooth again.

A few days later the old couple saw that the field next door was covered with molehills, but their lawn remained green and smooth.

Horses

Once upon a time a father and mother and their children went camping. They travelled far into the mountains. At last they found a field where they could pitch their tent. They were all tired from their journey and ready to sleep. Just as father was creeping into his sleeping bag he heard the sound of galloping horses coming nearer and nearer: Gallopa, gallopa, gallopa, gallopa. There they were snuffling round the tent, pulling at the ropes, stamping their hoofs and neighing loudly.

Father went outside and began to throw clods of earth at the horses and shouted at them to go away. Away they went.

So he snuggled into his sleeping bag and was getting ready to sleep when again he heard: Gallopa, gallopa, gallopa, gallopa. There were the horses again, snuffling round the tent, pulling at the ropes, stamping their hoofs and neighing loudly.

Father was cross. How could the family go to sleep? He jumped out of his sleeping bag, went outside and began to throw sticks at the horses. He shouted at them to go away. Once again, away they went. But very soon they came galloping back for the third time: Gallopa, gallopa, gallopa, gallopa. This time father stopped for a moment to think.

Then slowly he opened the tent flap and went out. "I am sorry," he said, "I know this is your field and we did not even ask whether we could spend the night here, but we have a long way to go tomorrow and the children are tired. We would be grateful if you would allow us to sleep – come back and wake us up at seven o'clock in the morning." He closed the flap and settled down once again into his sleeping bag. After a while the snuffling and stamping ceased and the horses went away.

The family slept peacefully and woke in the morning to the sound of the horses moving outside the tent. When father looked at his watch he saw that it was just seven o'clock.

The Boy and the Sea

Once upon a time there was a boy who lived by the sea. On the shore lay a large stone, and every day the boy went to the shore to sit on the stone, and to talk to the sea. The sea liked to see the boy sitting on the stone, so she whispered sea-stories to him. In the summer the boy would lie down flat on the stone and put his hands into the sea, and would tell the sea boy-stories. And so the sea whispered sea-stories and the boy told boy-stories.

One day the wind took the boy's hat away and did not give it back to him but instead gave it to the sea. Then the boy sat on his stone by the shore and waited until the sea returned his hat. The boy never told boy-stories to the wind because the wind took the boy-stories with him up into the sky and blew them around and told them to the whole world.

Winter was coming and one day the boy was again sitting on his stone by the shore. Then he saw that the wind and the sea were playing with each other. The wind whipped the water into the air and a thousand rainbow drops were flying around. And the sea ran up the shore and threw herself over the stone. Then the boy had to jump and run home or the sea would have taken him to her castle deep down below.

At home Mother said: "In the winter it is the wind's turn to play with the sea and in the summer it is your turn to play with the sea."

M. Tjelta

Little Madam

Once upon a time there was a Little Madam who had a pig. One day Little Madam wanted to go to a wedding. Then said Little Madam to the pig: "You must stay at home, Little Madam wants to go to the wedding." The pig grew angry and said:

"No, no, I want to go along too."

Then Little Madam went to the dog and said: "Dog, you must bite pig, pig will not stay at home, Little Madam wants to go to the wedding." Then the dog said:

"If pig does not do anything to me, then I will not do anything to him either."

Then Little Madam went to the stick and said: "Stick, you must beat dog, dog will not bite pig, pig will not stay at home, and Little Madam wants to go to the wedding." Then the stick said:

"If dog does not do anything to me, then I will not do anything to him either."

Then Little Madam went to the fire and said: "Fire, you must burn stick, stick will not beat dog, dog will not bite pig, pig will not stay at home, and Little Madam wants to go to the wedding." Then the fire said:

"If stick does not do anything to me, then I will not do anything to him either."

Then Little Madam went to the water and said: "Water, you must put out fire, fire will not burn stick, stick will not beat dog, dog will not bite pig, pig will not stay at home, and Little Madam wants to go to the wedding." Then the water said:

"If fire does not do anything to me, then I will not do anything to him either."

Then Little Madam went to the ox and said: "Ox, you must drink water, water will not put out fire, fire will not burn stick, stick will not beat dog, dog will not bite pig, pig will not stay at home and Little Madam wants to go to the wedding." Then the ox said:

"If water does not do anything to me, then I will not do anything to him either."

Then Little Madam went to the butcher and said: "Butcher, you must slaughter ox, ox will not drink water, water will not put out fire, fire will not burn stick, stick will not beat dog, dog will not bite pig, pig will not stay at home, and Little Madam wants to go to the wedding." Then the butcher said:

"Yes, I will slaughter the ox." And he went to the ox.

Then the ox said: "Oh, oh, oh, rather than be slaughtered I will drink the water."

Then the water said: "Lo, lo, lo, rather than be drunk I will put out the fire."

Then the fire said: "Hiss, hiss, hiss, rather than be put out I will burn the stick."

Then the stick said: "Thump, thump, thump, rather than be burnt I will beat the dog."

Then the dog said: "Bow, wow, wow, rather than be beaten I will bite the pig."

Then the pig said: "Ow, ow, ow, rather than be bitten I will stay at home."

So Little Madam could go to the wedding.

From Germany

Little Flea and Little Louse

J. Aulie

Lit - tle Flea and lit - tle Louse, they
lived to - ge - ther in one house.
Lit - tle Louse and lit - tle Flea,
see how they laughed so mer - ri - ly.

Little Louse and Little Flea

One day Little Flea said to Little Louse: "Little Louse, I'll go and carry the corn to the mill. Take care of yourself and see that you don't fall into the saucepan!"

"Ha, Ha, Ha," laughed Little Louse, "do not fear, I shall not fall into the saucepan!" And Little Flea went away. Little Louse began to sweep the house, to wash the crockery, to clean the saucepan and to kindle the fire. And there stood the saucepan filled with soup. Tired with all the work, Little Louse ran into the garden and laid himself down to sleep beneath the rosebush. Soon he was fast asleep.

After a while, Little Flea returned home. When he saw the door open he was greatly frightened. "Little Louse, where are you?" he called. But there was no answer, for Little Louse was fast asleep beneath the rosebush, and could not hear him calling.

Little Flea looked here, Little Flea looked there, but he could not find Little Louse. And in the saucepan the soup was boiling.

"Oh, woe is me!" Little Flea lamented, "Little Louse has surely fallen into the saucepan and been burnt. Oh, woe is me, I shan't stay here any more, I'll go into the wide world." When he had taken a few steps, the Table asked:

"Little Flea, why do you weep?"

"Oh, why should I not weep? Little Louse has fallen into the saucepan and been burnt, and I won't stay at home by myself!" The Table said:

"If from here you would be gone,
Then I'll come with you along!"

He lifted his legs and tottered after Little Flea. They passed the Baking Trough who asked: "Little Flea, why are you weeping?"

"Oh, why should I not weep? Little Louse has fallen into the saucepan and been burnt and I am not staying at home by myself and the Table is coming with me." The Baking Trough said:

"If you and the Table from here be gone,
Then I'll come with you along!"

He gave a jerk and tumbled after the Table. When they had reached the Door, the Door asked: "Little Flea, why are you weeping?"

"Oh, why should I not weep? Little Louse has fallen into the saucepan and been burnt and I am not staying at home by myself and the Table and the Baking Trough are coming along with me." And the Door lifted itself off its hinges and tumbled after the Baking Trough. When they reached the Tree, he asked:

"Little Flea, why are you weeping?"

"Oh, why should I not weep? Little Louse has fallen into the saucepan and been burnt and I am not staying at home by myself and the Table and the Baking Trough and the Door are coming with me!" The Tree pulled his roots out of the earth and swaggered after the Door.

They all arrived together at the rosebush. Just then Little Louse woke up. His eyes grew large when he saw the whole company sadly tottering along. But Little Flea, the Table, the Baking Trough, the Door and the Tree could hardly believe their eyes when they suddenly saw Little Louse happily jumping up in the garden.

First Little Louse laughed, then Little Flea laughed, then the Table laughed, then the Baking Trough laughed, then the Door laughed, then the Tree laughed: Ha, ha, Ha, Ha! They all returned merrily to the house. The Tree stretched his roots into the earth, the Door swung back onto his hinges, the Baking Trough put himself into the corner, the Table placed himself in the middle of the room, Little Flea sat himself at the table, Little Louse dished up the soup and both sat down happily together to eat it.

From France

116

The Boy and the Gram

Once a little boy was sitting on the doorsill of his home eating a handful of gram. As he was about to eat the last of the small round grain it slipped from his fingers and fell into a crack in the doorsill. The little boy cried:

"Oh doorsill, give me my gram.
My gram has stuck in you."

But the doorsill did not give it to him. Then the boy went to the carpenter and cried:

"Oh carpenter, split open the doorsill.
My gram has stuck in it."

The carpenter asked: "Do you think for the sake of one paltry grain of gram, I will split open the doorsill?" Then the boy went to the king and cried:

"Oh king, punish the carpenter.
The carpenter will not split open the doorsill,
And my gram has stuck in it."

The king asked: "Do you think for the sake of one paltry grain of gram, I will punish the carpenter?" Then the boy went to the queen and cried:

"Oh queen, sulk before the king.
The king will not punish the carpenter.
The carpenter will not split open the doorsill,
And my gram has stuck in it."

The queen asked: "Do you think for the sake of one paltry grain of gram, I will sulk before the king?" Then the boy went to the mouse and cried:

"Oh mouse, gnaw the clothes of the queen.
The queen will not sulk before the king.
The king will not punish the carpenter.
The carpenter will not split open the doorsill,
And my gram has stuck in it."

The mouse asked: "Do you think for the sake of one paltry grain of gram, I will gnaw the clothes of the queen?" Then the boy went to the cat, and cried:

"Oh cat, catch the mouse.
The mouse will not gnaw the clothes of the queen.
The queen will not sulk before the king.
The king will not punish the carpenter.
The carpenter will not split open the doorsill,
And my gram has stuck in it."

The cat asked: "Do you think for the sake of one paltry grain of gram, I will catch the mouse?" Then the boy went to the dog and cried:

"Oh dog, chase the cat.
The cat will not catch the mouse.
The mouse will not gnaw the clothes of the queen.
The queen will not sulk before the king.
The king will not punish the carpenter.
The carpenter will not split open the doorsill,
And my gram has stuck in it."

The dog asked: "Do you think for the sake of one paltry grain of gram, I will chase the cat?" Then the boy went to the stick and cried:

"Oh stick, beat the dog.
The dog will not chase the cat.
The cat will not catch the mouse.
The mouse will not gnaw the clothes of the queen.
The queen will not sulk before the king.

The king will not punish the carpenter.
The carpenter will not split open the doorsill,
And my gram has stuck in it."

The stick asked: "Do you think for the sake of one paltry grain of gram, I will beat the dog?" Then the boy went to the fire and cried:

"Oh fire, burn the stick.
The stick will not beat the dog.
The dog will not chase the cat.
The cat will not catch the mouse.
The mouse will not gnaw the clothes of the queen.
The queen will not sulk before the king.
The king will not punish the carpenter.
The carpenter will not split open the doorsill,
And my gram has stuck in it."

The fire asked: "Do you think for the sake of one paltry grain of gram, I will burn the stick?" Then the boy went to the sea and cried:

"Oh sea, quench the fire.
The fire will not burn the stick.
The stick will not beat the dog.
The dog will not chase the cat.
The cat will not catch the mouse.
The mouse will not gnaw the clothes of the queen.
The queen will not sulk before the king.
The king will not punish the carpenter.
The carpenter will not split open the doorsill,
And my gram has stuck in it."

The sea asked: "Do you think for the sake of one paltry grain of gram, I will quench the fire?" Then the boy went to the elephant and cried:

"Oh elephant, drink up the sea.
The sea will not quench the fire.
The fire will not burn the stick.
The stick will not beat the dog.
The dog will not chase the cat.
The cat will not catch the mouse.
The mouse will not gnaw the clothes of the queen.
The queen will not sulk before the king.
The king will not punish the carpenter.
The carpenter will not split open the doorsill,
And my gram has stuck in it."

The elephant asked: "Do you think for the sake of one paltry grain of gram, I will drink up the sea?" Then the boy went to the ant and cried:

"Oh ant, crawl up the elephant's ear and worry him.
The elephant will not drink up the sea.
The sea will not quench the fire.
The fire will not burn the stick.
The stick will not beat the dog.
The dog will not chase the cat.
The cat will not catch the mouse.
The mouse will not gnaw the clothes of the queen.
The queen will not sulk before the king.
The king will not punish the carpenter.
The carpenter will not split open the doorsill,
And my gram has stuck in it."

"What will you give me if I crawl in the elephant's ear and worry him?" asked the ant.

"I will give you some sugar," replied the boy. Then he gave the ant some sugar, and it crawled into the elephant's ear and started to worry him.

Then the elephant started to drink up the sea.
The sea started to quench the fire.
The fire started to burn the stick.
The stick started to beat the dog.
The dog started to chase the cat.
The cat started to chase the mouse.
The mouse started to gnaw the clothes of the queen.
The queen started to sulk before the king.
The king started to punish the carpenter.
The carpenter started to split open the doorsill.
Then the doorsill gave up the gram, and the little boy ate it.

From India

The Rooster and the Sultan

Once upon a time there lived a very poor old woman who had nothing at all in the world except one little small rooster. This rooster was scratching the ground one day, looking for something to eat, when suddenly what should he find but a shiny penny! Now it chanced just then that a big fat man came along. He was called Sultan of the Land of Turkey and he came strutting up the street wearing big baggy pantaloons, red shoes with upturned toes and a bright red turban on his head. Well, the sultan noticed the penny glittering there in the dust and he said to the little small rooster, "Rooster, give me that penny!"

But the little small rooster said, "No! I will give my mistress this penny, for she is poor and she needs it."

Then the sultan snatched the penny away from the little small rooster. He stuck up his nose in the air and he marched off home with the penny.

The rooster was ready to cry, but he gave himself a good shake. He ruffled up his feathers as if getting ready to fight. He lifted his head up high, and he hurried after the sultan. He ran into the sultan's garden, and hopped onto the fence.

"Cock-a-doodle-doo!" he cried. "Give me back my penny!"

What a noise! The sultan clapped his hands to his ears. He ran as fast as he could to the most distant room in his great big, enormous palace. But the little small rooster followed him and perched on his window sill.

"Cock-a-doodle-doo!" he cried. "Give me back my penny."

The Sultan got angrier and angrier. He called a slave and said, "Get that rooster, slave, and throw him in the well!"

So the slave went and caught the rooster and, bang! He plopped him in the well. But the rooster kept his wits about him and began to say a charm:

> "Suck the water up, my throat!
> Suck the water, all the water. Suck the water up!"

So the little small rooster's throat sucked up all the water and he was safe on dry ground. Then he flew to the sultan's window. And once again he cried, "Cock-a-doodle-doo! Give me back my penny!"

Well, the sultan was in a rage. He called a slave and said, "Go slave, get that rooster and throw him in the fire!"

So the slave caught the little small rooster and threw him in a roaring fire. But the little small rooster cried:

> "Pour out the water, my throat! All the water, pour it!
> Put this big fire out!"

Instantly his throat poured all the water from the well into the leaping flames. The fire died down with a hiss. And the rooster was safe again. Then he flew to the sultan's window and cried as he had before, "Cock-a-doodle-doo! Give me back my penny!"

Well, the sultan was now so angry he couldn't think what to do next. But he called a slave and said, "Go slave, get that rooster and throw him in a bee-hive. The bees will sting him well! They'll end this terrible crowing!"

So the slave caught the rooster again and threw him in a bee-hive. But the rooster started singing:

> "Suck the bees, my throat! Suck the bees all up!
> Suck the bees all up!"

Then his throat sucked up the bees and the little rooster again rushed to the sultan's window.

"Cock-a-doodle-doo!" he cried. "Give me back my penny!"

The Sultan was beside himself! He just went raving mad. "Bring that rooster to me!" he thundered.

So the slave went and caught the rooster and brought him before the sultan. And the sultan, at the sight of the rooster, lost all the wits he had. He seized the little small rooster and stuffed him into the pocket of his big, baggy pantaloons. "Now I have you, I'll keep you," he shrieked, "so you don't get out again!"

But the little small rooster sang:

"Pour out the bees, my throat! Pour the bees all out!
Pour the bees all out!"

And his throat poured the bees all out in the sultan's pantaloons. The bees began to sting the sultan. They stung him and stung him and stung him. The sultan screeched and he screeched! He slapped at his pantaloons! He danced on one foot! But he could not stop that stinging. So at last he yelled to a slave, "Give this rooster back his penny and let him go from the palace! I must have peace again!"

So the slaves cut a great big slit in the sultan's pantaloons. Out flew the little small rooster and the swarm of angry bees. Then the Sultan heaved a sigh of relief. The slaves gave the rooster his penny and let him go from the palace. And the little small rooster flew home and gave the poor woman the penny. The old woman bought all she needed to make herself cosy and comfortable and she and the little small rooster lived happily ever after.

From Hungary

The Goat and the Ram

Once upon a time there lived a man and his wife, and they had a goat and a ram.

One day the man said to his wife: "Look here, let's get rid of the goat and the ram; why, they only keep eating our corn, and don't help to feed us at all."

So he told them: "Be off, goat and ram, and don't dare to show yourselves at my gate ever again."

Then the goat and the ram made themselves a bag, and off they went. They went on and on, until they saw a wolf's head lying in the middle of the field."

They picked up the head, put it into their bag, and went on again. They went on and on, until they saw a fire burning, and they said: "Let's go and spend the night there, lest the wolves should eat us." But when they got there, lo and behold! It was the wolves themselves who were cooking their porridge, and so they said: "Good evening, young fellows, and good appetite to you!" And the wolves answered: "Good evening Mister Goat and Mister Ram. We're just boiling our porridge, come and have some, and then we'll eat you both up." At this the goat took fright, while as for the ram, his legs had been shaking with fear for some time. Then the goat began to think, and he thought and thought and at last he said: "Come now, Mister Ram, let's have a look at that wolf's head you've got in your sack!" And the Ram took out the wolf's head, when the goat said: "No, not that one. Let's have the other bigger one!" And again the ram gave him the same head, but he said: "No, not that one either! Let's have the largest of all!"

And the wolves looked and thought the ram had a sackful of wolves' heads and each one of them said to himself: "Well, these are nice guests to have! I'd better hop off!" And first one said aloud to the others: "I like your company alright, brothers, but somehow, the porridge doesn't seem to be boiling very well. I'll just run and fetch some sticks to throw on the fire." And as he went off, he thought to himself: "You and your company be bothered!" And he never came back.

Then the second wolf kept thinking how he could get away, and he said: "It seems very funny, our brother went to fetch the wood, but he hasn't brought the wood, and hasn't come back himself. I'll just go and help him!" So off he went too, and never came back. And the third wolf was left sitting there, and at last he said: "I must really go and hurry them up. What are they dawdling all this time for!" And as soon as he was gone, he set off running and never so much as looked back.

At that the goat and the ram were delighted. They ate up all the porridge and then ran away themselves.

Meanwhile, the wolves had all three met and they said to each other: "Look here, why were we three frightened of the goat and the ram? They're no stronger than we, after all! Let's go and eat them for supper."

But when they came back to the fire, there was not so much as a trace of them left. Then the wolves set off in pursuit, and at last they saw them, where they had climbed up a tree, the goat on an upper and the ram on a lower branch. So the eldest wolf lay down under the tree and began to show his teeth, looking up at them, and waiting for them to climb down. And the ram who was trembling all over from fright, suddenly fell down right on top of the wolf, and at the same moment the goat shouted out from up above: "There, that's the one! Get me the largest of all!" And the wolf was terrified, because he thought the ram had jumped down after him, and you should just have seen him run! The other two wolves followed after.

And that is the end of my tale.

From Russia

126

leaving, he would tell Masha to stay in the hut and wait for him.

"You must never go out without me," he would say. "If you do, I will catch you and eat you up!"

So Masha set to thinking how to run away from the bear. All around was the forest and there was no one to ask which way to go.

At last she knew what to do.

That day, when the bear came back from the forest, Masha said to him:

"Bear, Bear, do let me go to my village for a day. I want to take something good to eat to my grandmother and grandfather."

"No, that will not do at all," said the bear. "You will get lost in the forest. Give me whatever it is you want them to have, and I shall take it to them myself."

Now that was what Masha wanted!

She baked some pies, put them on a plate, and, getting out a large basket, said to the bear: "I shall put the pies in the basket, and you can take it to my grandmother and grandfather. But mind, you are not to open the basket on the way and you are not to eat the pies. I am going to climb an oak tree and I shall be sitting there and watching you!"

"Very well, give me the basket," the bear replied.

"Go out on the porch first, and see if it is raining," Masha said.

The bear went out on the porch, and Masha at once crawled into the basket and put the plate of pies on her head.

The bear came in, and there was the basket all ready for him! So he put it on his back and set off for the village.

Tramp-tramp went the bear amid the spruce trees, clumpety-clump went he amid the birch trees; up hill and down dale ran his long, winding trail. On and on he walked without a stop until at last he was tired and fit to drop.

> "If I don't rest my bones
> I think I shall die,
> So, I'll sit on a stump
> And eat a pie!"

said the bear.

129

But Masha called out from the basket:

> "I see you! I see you!
> Don't sit on the stump
> And don't eat my pie,
> But take it to Grandma
> And Grandpa, say I!"

"Dear me, what sharp eyes Masha has," said the bear. "She sees everything!"

He picked up the basket and went on.

He walked and he walked until he could walk no more. So he stopped and said:

> "If I don't rest my bones
> I think I shall die,
> So, I'll sit on a stump
> And eat a pie!"

But Masha called out again from the basket:

> "I see you! I see you!
> Don't sit on the stump
> And don't eat my pie,
> But take it to Grandma
> And Grandpa, say I!"

The bear was astonished.

"What a clever girl Masha is!" said he. "She is sitting high up in a tree and she is far away, but she sees all I do and she hears all I say!"

He got to his feet and walked on even faster than before.

He came to the village and, finding the house where Masha's grandmother and grandfather lived, began to bang away at the gate with all his might: KNOCK-KNOCK-KNOCK!

"Open the gate! I have brought you something nice from Masha!" he cried.

But the village dogs scented the bear and rushed out at him from every yard, yelping and barking.

The bear was frightened, he set down the basket by the gate and away he ran to the forest without once looking back!

The old man and the old woman came up to the gate and they saw the basket.

"What is in the basket?" the old woman asked.

The old man lifted the top, he looked and he could not believe his eyes. For there in the basket sat Masha, alive and well.

The old man and the old woman were overjoyed. They kissed and embraced Masha.

From Russia

The Wonderful Pot

A man and his wife were once living in a very small cottage – the smallest and poorest hut in the whole village. They were so poor that they often lacked even their daily bread. They had been obliged to sell nearly everything they had, but had managed somehow to keep their only cow. At length they decided that the cow, too, must go, and the man led her away, intending to take her to market. As he walked along the road a stranger hailed him, asking if he intended to sell the animal, and how much he would take for it.

"I think," answered he, "that a hundred crowns would be a fair price."

"Money I cannot give you," said the stranger, "but I have something which is worth as much as a hundred crowns. Here is a pot which I am willing to exchange for your cow." And he showed the man an iron pot with three legs and a handle.

"A pot!" exclaimed the cow's owner. "What possible use would that be to me when I have nothing to put in it? My wife and children cannot eat an iron pot. No, money is what I need and what I must have."

While the two men looked at each other and at the cow and the pot, the three-legged thing suddenly began to speak. "Just take me," it said. The poor man thought that if the pot could speak, no doubt it could do more than that. So he closed the bargain, took the pot, and returned home with it.

When he reached his hut he went first to the stall where the cow had been tied, for he was afraid to appear before his wife at once. He tied the pot to the manger, went into the hut, and asked for something to eat. He was hungry from his long walk.

"Well," said his wife, "did you make a good bargain at the market? Did you get a good price for the cow?"

"Yes," he said, "the price was fair enough."

"That is well," she returned. "The money will help us a long time."

"No," he sighed, "I received no money for the cow."

"Dear me!" she cried. "What did you receive, then?" He told her to go and look in the cow's stall.

As soon as the woman learned that the three-legged pot was all that had been paid him for the cow, she scolded and berated her husband. "You are a great blockhead!" she cried. "I wish I myself had taken the cow to market! I never heard of such foolishness!" Thus she went on and on.

But, "Clean me and put me on the fire," suddenly shouted the pot.

The woman opened her eyes in wonder, and now it was her turn to think that if the pot could talk, no doubt it could do more than this. She cleaned and washed it carefully and put it on the fire.

"I skip, I skip!" cried the pot.

"How far do you skip?" asked the woman.

"To the rich man's house, to the rich man's house!" it answered, running from the fireplace to the door, across the yard, and up the road, as fast as its three short legs would carry it.

The rich man, who had never shared anything with the poor, lived not very far away. His wife was baking bread when the pot came running in and jumped up on the table. "Ah," exclaimed the woman, "isn't this wonderful! I need you for a pudding that must be baked at once." Thereupon she began to heap good things into the pot: flour, sugar, butter, raisins, almonds, spices, and so on. And the pot received it all with a good will. At length the pudding was made, but when the rich man's wife reached for it, intending to put it on the stove, tap, tap, tap went the three short legs, and the pot stood on the threshold of the open door. "Dear me, where are you going with my pudding?" cried the woman.

"To the poor man's home," replied the pot, running down the road at great speed.

When the poor couple saw the pot skipping back to them, with the pudding in it, they rejoiced. The man lost no time in asking his wife whether the bargain did not seem to be an excellent one, after all.

"Yes," she agreed. She was pleased and contented.

Next morning the pot cried again, "I skip, I skip!"

"How far do you skip?" they asked.

"To the rich man's barn!" it shouted, running up the road. When it arrived at the barn it hopped through the doorway. "Look at that black pot!" cried the men, who were threshing wheat. "Let us see how much it will hold." They poured a bushel of wheat into it, but it did not seem to fill. Another bushel went in, but there was still more room. When every grain of wheat had been given to the pot, it seemed capable of holding still more. But as there was no more wheat to be found, the three short legs began to move, and when the men looked around, the pot had reached the gate.

"Stop, stop!" they called. "Where are you going with our wheat?"

"To the poor man's home," replied the pot, speeding down the road and leaving the men behind, dismayed and dumbfounded.

The poor people were delighted. The wheat they received was enough to feed them for several years.

On the third morning, the pot again skipped up the road. It was a beautiful day. The sun shone so brightly that the rich man had spread his money on a table near his open window to allow the sunshine to clear the mould from his gold. All at once the pot stood on the table before him. He was counting his coins, as wealthy men like to do, and although he could not imagine where this black pot had come from, he thought it would make a fine place to store his money. So he threw in one handful of coins after another, until the pot held them all. At that very moment the pot jumped from the table to the window sill.

"Wait!" shouted the man. "Where are you going with all my money?"

"To the poor man's home," returned the pot, skipping down the road with the money dancing within it. In the centre of the poor man's hut it stopped, and when its owners saw the unexpected treasure, they cried out in rapture.

"Clean and wash me," said the pot, "and put me aside."

Next morning the pot announced that it was ready to skip.

"How far do you skip?" asked the man and his wife.

"To the rich man's house!" So it ran up the road again, never stopping until it had reached the rich man's kitchen. The man happened to be there himself this time, and as soon as he saw the pot he cried, "There is that pot that carried away our pudding, our wheat, and all our money! I shall make it return what it stole!"

The man flung himself upon the pot, but found that he was unable to get off again.

"I skip, I skip!" shouted the pot.

"Skip to the North Pole, if you wish!" yelled the man, furiously trying to free himself. But the three short legs moved on, carrying him rapidly down the road. The poor man and his wife saw it pass their door, but it never thought of stopping. For all that I know, it went straight on, carrying its burden to the North Pole.

The poor couple were now rich. They thought often of the wonderful pot with the three short legs that skipped so cheerfully for their good. But it was gone, and they have never seen it since.

From Denmark

The Hungry Cat

Once upon a time there lived a man and a cat. Said the peasant: "Good day, Cat! How are you? Have you had something to eat?"

And the cat answers: "Oh, no – not much. Only a little platter of milk and a tiny platter of fat and I am still so hungry. And since I am so hungry I must look for something to eat."

Then the cat goes into the stable and there she sees a calf and talks to him and, as she is still so hungry, she devours the calf. Then the cat goes to the gate and there she sees the cow outside the gate.

Says the cow: "Good day, Cat! How are you? Have you had something to eat?"

And the cat answers: "Oh, no – not much. Only a little platter of milk and a tiny platter of fat and the calf in the stable. And I am still so hungry. And as I am so hungry I must eat you too!" And she devours the cow.

Then the cat goes to the meadow and there she sees the bull. Says the bull: "Good day, Cat! How are you? Have you had something to eat?"

And the cat answers: "Oh, no – not much. Only a little platter of milk and a tiny platter of fat and the calf in the stable and the cow outside the gate. And I am still so hungry. And as I am so hungry I must eat you too!" And she devours the bull.

And now the cat wanders into the wide world. There in the road she sees a many-coloured crowd. A wedding procession is driving along. In the first coach sit the bride and the bridegroom. In the second, third and fourth coaches sit the wedding guests. In the fifth coach sit the cook and the kitchen boys with plentiful dishes and drinks and many fine titbits – such as you could not keep on your tongue. In the sixth and seventh coaches sit the musicians, the drummers, the pipers and the double bass singers. The whole wedding procession says to the cat: "Good day, Cat! How are you? Have you had something to eat?"

And the cat answers all the people, right down to the double bass singer: "Oh, no – not much. Only a little platter of milk and a tiny platter of fat, and the calf in the stable, and the cow outside the gate and the bull in the meadow. And I am still so hungry. And as I am so hungry I must eat all of you too." And then the cat begins to eat. And she devours first the bride and the bridegroom in the first coach. Then the wedding guests in the second, third and fourth coaches. Then the cook and the kitchen boys in the fifth coach, together with the plentiful dishes and drinks, and many fine titbits – such as you could not keep on your tongue. And the musicians in the sixth and seventh coaches – all the drummers, the pipers and double bass singers.

And now the cat goes up the mountain and there she sees the moon standing above the mountain. Says the moon: "Good day, Cat! How are you? Have you had something to eat?"

And the cat answers: "Oh, no – not much. Only a little platter of milk and a tiny platter of fat, and the calf in the stable, and the cow outside the gate, and the bull in the meadow and the wedding procession with the bride and the bridegroom in the first coach, with the wedding guests in the second, third and fourth coaches, with the cook and the kitchen boys in the fifth coach as they sat there with plentiful dishes and drinks and many fine titbits – such as you could not keep on your tongue, with the musicians in the sixth and seventh coaches, all the pipers, the drummers and double bass singers. And I am still so hungry. And as I am so hungry I must eat you too." And she devours the moon.

Now nothing holds her to the earth and she goes higher into the heavens. There she sees the sun. Says the sun: "Good day, Cat! How are you? Have you had something to eat?"

And the cat answers: "Oh, no – not much. Only a little platter of milk and a tiny platter of fat, and the calf in the stable, and the cow outside the gate, and the bull in the meadow and the wedding procession with the bride and the bridegroom in the first coach, with the wedding guests in the second, third and fourth coaches, with the cook and the kitchen boys in the fifth coach as they sat there with plentiful dishes and drinks and many fine titbits – such as you could not keep on your tongue, with the musicians in the sixth and seventh coaches, all the pipers, the drummers and double bass singers, and the moon above the mountain. And I am still so hungry.

And as I am so hungry I must eat you too." And she devours the sun.

How dark the world had become!

Then the cat groped her way further through the heavens and came to a big, big bridge. On the bridge she met a goat with beautiful golden horns. Said the goat: "Good day, Cat! How are you? Have you had something to eat?"

And the cat answers: "Oh, no – not much. Only a little platter of milk and a tiny platter of fat, and the calf in the stable, and the cow outside the gate, and the bull in the meadow and the wedding procession with the bride and the bridegroom in the first coach, with the wedding guests in the second, third and fourth coaches, with the cook and the kitchen boys in the fifth coach as they sat there with plentiful dishes and drinks and many fine titbits – such as you could not keep on your tongue, with the musicians in the sixth and seventh coaches, all the pipers, the drummers and double bass singers, and the moon above the mountain and the sun in the sky. And I am still so hungry. And as I am so hungry I must . . ."

"STOP !" called the goat. "That is a game that two can play!" And he charged against her belly with his horns so that the big, fat belly split open.

And out they all came.

First the sun in the sky, then the moon above the mountain, then the wedding procession with the seventh and sixth coaches, all the double bass singers, the pipers and drummers, the fifth coach with the kitchen boys and the cook as they sat there with many fine tit bits – such as you could not keep on your tongue, and plentiful drinks and dishes, and the fourth, third and second coaches with the wedding guests and the bridegroom and the bride in the first coach. Then came the bull from the meadow, the cow from outside the gate and the calf in the stable. And once again it was bright and light in the sky and on the earth, for the sun was shining again and the wicked cat was dead.

And they all danced and laughed, bounded and sang and by now they had become quite hungry. And it was all like one great big wedding procession.

From Norway

Four Friends

Long, long ago in a certain country there lived a washerman who owned an old donkey. When the donkey became so old that he could no longer work, the washerman drove him from the house.

With a heart full of sorrow, the donkey plodded down the road. Nearing the village, he met an old dog. The dog was sprawled in the dirt; there was a sad expression on his face. The donkey asked, "Brother Dog, why do you look so dejected?"

The dog replied, "Ah, what can I say? Because I have become old and feeble, my master has driven me from the house."

The donkey consoled him by saying, "Such is the world. We work hard for our masters, and when we are no longer useful, they send us from the house."

The donkey invited the dog to travel with him, and the friendless dog readily accepted. They had not gone far, when they encountered a cat. She was mewing pitifully. "What is the matter, Sister Cat?" the donkey asked kindly.

The cat wiped her eyes and replied, "What can I say? I am very old and cannot catch mice any more. Last night my master thrashed me and drove me from the house."

The dog bent his head in sympathy and said, "The same thing has happened to us. Men are such ungrateful creatures. Come, travel with us. You need companions at a time like this."

So the unhappy trio set off down the road. Soon they found a hen weeping by the roadside. Her feet were tied with a strong rope. The cat said, "Sister Hen, tell us what is the trouble?"

In a choked voice, the hen answered, "What can I say? I laid thousands of eggs for my master and presented thousands of chicks to him. Now that I am old and infirm, my master has decided to eat me."

"That is a woeful story," said the cat. "We also have encountered unhappiness." And one by one the donkey, the dog, and the cat narrated their stories. Then the cat gently untied the rope from the hen's feet and invited her to join them.

The four friends walked until evening when they found themselves at the edge of a forest. The cat with her sharp eyes peered into the foliage and spied a lighted house. She offered to go and investigate.

The cat crept upto the front window and discovered a gang of robbers. Around them was piled a treasure in gold and gems and other precious things. They were eating platters full of delicious food.

The cat ran back to her friends and told them what she had seen. Immediately the dog offered a plan. "Let us go back to the house. I have thought of a plan that will frighten the robbers out of their skin. Let me stand on the donkey's back, the cat will stand on the dog's back, and the hen will perch on the cat's head. Then we shall bark and miaow and bray and scream at the top of our lungs."

The other three agreed that this was a fine plan, and soon the four friends were standing on each other's back in front of the window. Then a great tumult was raised in the forest such as never had been heard before. Braying, crowing, barking, and miaowing mixed together to make a frightening noise. The robbers, thinking that they had been discovered, scattered into the forest and were never seen again.

The four friends moved into the house and spent their old age in luxury and contentment.

From *Pakistan*

Krencipal and Krencipalka

Krencipal and Krencipalka had not a penny to bless themselves with. Their cottage was tumbling to pieces; there was not a bite of bread in the cupboard. A bad state of things, to be sure!

"Let us go out in the world and seek our fortunes," said Krencipal to Krencipalka. So off they started.

And they walked and walked, until they met a needle.

"Where are you off to?" asked the needle. "Into the world to seek our fortunes," said Krencipal and Krencipalka. And the needle said,

> "Take me with you all the way,
> I will help you night and day."

"But how are we going to carry you?" asked Krencipal and Krencipalka.

"Just stick me in your hat," answered the needle. And they did so.

And they walked and walked until they met a lobster.

"Where are you off to?" asked the lobster. "Into the world to seek our fortunes," said Krencipal and Krencipalka. And the lobster said,

> "Take me with you all the way,
> I will help you night and day."

"But how are we going to carry you?" asked Krencipal and Krencipalka.

"Just put me in your basket," answered the lobster. And they did so.

And they walked and walked until they met a duck.

"Where are you off to?" asked the duck. "Into the world to seek our fortunes," said Krencipal and Krencipalka. And the duck said,

> "Take me with you all the way,
> I will help you night and day."

"But how are we going to carry you?" asked Krencipal and Krencipalka.

"Just put me in your sack," answered the duck. And they did so.

And they walked and walked until they met a cock. "Where are you off to?" asked the cock. "Into the world to seek our fortunes," said Krencipal and Krencipalka. And the cock said,

> "Take me with you all the way,
> I will help you night and day."

"But how are we going to carry you?" asked Krencipal and Krencipalka.

"Just put me in with the duck," answered the cock. And they did so.

And they walked and walked until they met a pig.

"Where are you off to?" asked the pig. "Into the world to seek our fortunes," said Krencipal and Krencipalka. And the pig said,

> "Take me with you all the way,
> I will help you night and day."

"But how are we going to carry you?" asked Krencipal and Krencipalka.

"You don't have to carry me," answered the pig. "Just drive me in front of you." And they did so.

And they walked and walked until they met an ox.

"Where are you off to?" asked the ox. "Into the world to seek our fortunes," said Krencipal and Krencipalka. And the ox said,

> "Take me with you all the way,
> I will help you night and day."

"Likely we're going to carry you!" said Krencipal and Krencipalka.

"You don't need to carry me," answered the ox. "I'll carry the misses and the basket as well." And so he did.

And they walked and walked until they met a horse.

"Where are you off to?" asked the horse. "Into the world to seek our fortunes," said Krencipal and Krencipalka. And the horse said,

"Take me with you all the way,
I will help you night and day."

"Likely we're going to carry you!" said Krencipal and Krencipalka.

"You don't need to carry me," answered the horse. "I'll carry you and the sack as well." And so he did.

So Krencipal sat on the horse, Krencipalka sat on the ox, the basket was hung on the ox's horns, the sack was hung on the horse's tail, and the pig ran on in front. And they walked and walked until they came to a wood.

In this wood was a fine house in which no Christian soul might live, for it was inhabited by a wicked goblin.

Krencipal and Krencipalka went into the house, the horse went into the stable, the ox went into the barn, the pig went into the sty, the cock went into the parlour, the duck went behind the kitchen stove, the lobster went into a bucket of water, and the needle went, eye downwards, into a bench in front of the table.

The pig told them to put some acorns to roast for him, and they did so.

After a while in came the goblin.

"What are you doing here, Krencipal and Krencipalka?" he asked.

"We are just passing the night here," they replied. "Pray, sit down." And so he did. And the needle ran into him, for he had seated himself upon the bench.

"Oh! Oh! Oh!" cried the goblin, and ran to the bucket for water to bathe the prick. When he put his hand into the bucket the lobster seized it and squeezed it until the bones cracked.

"Oh! Oh! Oh!" cried the goblin, and ran to the fire for ashes to rub on his hand. But the acorns went bang! bang! bang! and flew out and hit him in the eye.

"E! E! E!" cried the goblin, and ran to the barn for some straw that he might wipe his eye, but the ox caught him on its horns and threw him over its head into the stable, where the horse was standing; then the horse let out with his hind legs and sent the goblin flying through the yard into the kitchen and out by the front door. As he passed the duck said, "Quack, quack, quack, quack, quack," and the cock said, "Tuck, tuck, tuck, tuck,"

The goblin took to his heels and ran as fast as he could to the Underworld.

"What are you doing here?" asked his friends. "Why are you not at home?"

Home?" cried the goblin, his teeth chattering so that he could hardly speak. "N-n-n-ever a-g-g-g-ain!" He sat down to get over his fright, but it was some time before his teeth stood still so that he could tell them what had happened to him.

"My house is haunted by humans," he said as soon as he could speak. " I found two of them sitting at the table and they asked me to take a bit of dinner with them. So I sat down on the bench, and the cook was crouched under the table and ran a skewer into me. I went to get some water to bathe the prick and there was a tinker, sitting in the bucket, who pinched my hand so hard with his pincers that the bones cracked. I went to the fire to get some ashes to rub my hand with, and there was a soldier, who shot at me – bang! bang! bang! – and hit me clean in the eye. I went to the barn for some straw to wipe my eye, and there was a haymaker, who tossed me up into the air with his pitchfork and right over into the stable. And there was a blacksmith, who gave me such a knock with his hammer that I went flying through the yard, into the kitchen and out by the front door. As I passed, another of these creatures called out, "Smack-smack-smack-smack-smack-him w-e-ll!" and another, "Chuck-chuck-chuck-chuck-chuck-him o-u-t!" And I'll never go home again!"

So Krencipal and Krencipalka stayed on in the fine house and lived there happily ever after.

From Poland

144

The Saucepan with the Hollah-Bollah Potbelly

There was once an old woman. She was very poor and had nothing more to eat. She searched in her boxes and baskets; she looked in all her cupboards. At last, she found a little meal and with that she cooked a soup. When she had eaten it she washed the saucepan with the hollah-bollah potbelly quite clean. She put it on the windowsill to dry and said: "Now I shall surely have to starve unless the good God sends help." She sat herself in her armchair and fell asleep. Then the sun came along and shone into the saucepan with the hollah-bollah potbelly until it was dry. Then the saucepan said: "I'm off, hoppety-hop."

The sun asked: "Saucepan, where are you going hoppety-hop?" – "I'm going hoppety-hop to the market to fetch food for the poor old woman." And the saucepan sprang off the windowsill and went hoppety-hop into the town to the market. There it ran among the market folk.

Along came a peasant who had a sack full of beans, and did not know where to put them. "Saucepan," said he, when he saw the saucepan standing there, "you've come just at the right moment. I can make use of you." He shook a whole lot of beans into the hollah-bollah potbelly. Hardly had the saucepan felt that his potbelly was full than it exclaimed: "Now I'm off, hoppety-hop." It turned round and ran back to the poor old woman. Then it knocked on the door and called out: "Open up, open up, the saucepan with the hollah-bollah potbelly is back again." She woke up and ran to the door to open it. How delighted she was when she saw the saucepan with the hollah-bollah potbelly with the lovely fat beans in it. She cooked a bean soup, ate it, scrubbed the saucepan quite clean again, put it on the window sill to dry and thought: "The good God has helped me once, he sent the saucepan, will he help me a second time?" Then she fell asleep again.

Again the sun appeared, and shone into the saucepan with the hollah-bollah potbelly until it dried.

Then the saucepan said: "Now I'm off hoppety-hop into the town to fetch food for the poor old woman."

It ran into the town where it sprang into the butcher's shop right onto the serving counter. The butcher's wife was standing behind it with a ladle full of meat broth in her hand. She didn't know what to do with it. Then she saw the saucepan and cried: "You've come just at the right moment. "And she poured the meat broth into the saucepan with its hollah-bollah potbelly. The saucepan felt its hollah-bollah potbelly grow warm and full. It sprang off the serving counter and went hoppety-hop back to the old woman. It knocked on the door and called out: "The saucepan is here with the hollah-bollah potbelly, open the door for me!"

Oh, how delighted the old woman was! She opened the door, brought the saucepan in and drank the warm meat broth.

Then she scrubbed the saucepan beautifully clean again and put it on the windowsill to dry. Once more the sun came and dried it with its rays. When these shone so beautifully into the hollah-bollah potbelly the saucepan said: "Now off I go hoppety-hop." – "Saucepan, dear Saucepan," asked the sun, "where are you going hoppety-hop this time?"

"I'm going hoppety-hop to the rich man to fetch money for the poor old woman." And sure enough the saucepan went hoppety-hop to the rich man right into the middle of his room. The rich man was just sitting at his table counting a heap of money. He was thinking that he had so much that he didn't know where to put it. Then he saw the saucepan with the hollah-bollah potbelly and cried: "You've come just at the right moment." He shook a heap of money into the hollah-bollah potbelly. No sooner had the saucepan felt it was full than it jumped off the table and called out: "Now I'm off, hoppety-hop!"

"Alas, alas," shouted the man, because the saucepan was out of the door, running along the street and disappearing.

The saucepan knocked at the old woman's door and called: "Open up, open up, the saucepan with the hollah-bollah potbelly is here!" The woman hastened to open the door. When she saw so many gold pieces she did not take the time to scrub the saucepan. She did not set it either on the windowsill in the sun, but she chased it out of doors and called

146

out: "Saucepan, run quickly once more to the rich man and fetch me some more, more, more!"

Then the saucepan grew angry and muttered: "Right, now I'm off hoppety-hop!"

It did not go hoppety-hop to the rich man. It ran into the market and placed itself under a cow. It stayed until the cow lifted its tail and let something drop. That was a round blob. It did not smell good, poof!

The saucepan, however, feeling its hollah-bollah potbelly full again turned and went hoppety-hop back to the old woman. "Open up, open up," it called, "the saucepan with the hollah-bollah potbelly is here!"

The woman was waiting in the doorway. When she saw what was in the saucepan she was so furiously angry that she took the saucepan and threw it with a good swing out of the window. Now she had no more saucepan.

The saucepan went hoppety-hop into the wide world and never came back. It is still running. Perhaps you will meet it somewhere.

From Germany

The Three Oranges

Once upon a time there lived a prince, young and happy at heart. When he had grown up, he went to look for a bride, but he only wanted one who was not born of an ordinary mother. Such a one was not to be found in the whole kingdom, and so he decided to go forth into the wide world. He took nothing with him, but three loaves of bread and the blessing of his father.

"When you have found the maiden come home and tell me, so that we can prepare your wedding feast," thus spoke the old king.

The prince wandered for a long time; at last he came to a crossroads and didn't know in which direction to continue. There sat an old man, who could hardly see or hear and was begging for food. The prince gave him a loaf of bread, and then the old man rose and said: "Now I can be of service to you – tell me what you are looking for." The prince told him about his wish and the old man said: "You are on the right road, go straight ahead and you will come to a castle which is being guarded by a mighty lion. When he leaps at you, be without fear and throw a loaf of bread into his jaws, and he will not harm you. Go past him with courage, and the gate will open of its own accord. In the hall you will find three oranges and when you open one, a beautiful maiden will arise. Take care though, that she receives a drink of water immediately, otherwise she will wither as fast as she blossomed forth."

The prince thanked the old man for his advice and went on his way. He reached the castle and a roaring lion leapt at him. Then he threw the second loaf of bread into his jaws and the lion lay down peacefully at his feet. The gate sprang open and he stepped into the hall. Before him stood a table with three oranges upon it. He opened the first orange and there arose from it a gentle figure but before he could turn round to fetch some water, she withered away as quickly as she had blossomed forth.

With great impatience he opened the second orange and again a beautiful maiden stood before him but, as he had no water to hand, she vanished like the first one.

Now, only one orange was left and the prince looked for water to have ready when the time came, even before he opened the fruit. Then he noticed a lake near the castle, surrounded by tall poplar trees. To this place he carried the third orange, and put it down on the shore and opened it.

A charming maiden, more beautiful than the other two, appeared before him. He bent down and gave her a drink. She lived, and came to him, smiled and stretched out her hand. Happily they strolled along the edge of the lake, then the prince spoke: "Wait here for me, dearest, while I hasten to my father, so that he can prepare our wedding feast. In the meantime climb the tree and wait until I return."

"Don't stay away too long," she said, "I am afraid when I am alone." She climbed the poplar tree, hid in its branches, and the prince went on his way. However, it was far to go, and when evening came, he grew tired and sat on a stone and fell asleep on the spot.

In the meantime, a witch came up to the lake to wash her clothes. In the mirror of the water she saw the reflection of the girl in the branches. "Do come down from the tree, beautiful maiden," called the old woman. "Come, I want to comb your golden hair so that it shines in the moonlight when your prince comes to fetch you." The unsuspecting girl climbed down, but hardly had the witch's comb touched her hair, than she changed into a white dove which flew up into the air and sang:

> Silent, silent, silent,
> Trapped in a magic circle,
> I became a little white dove,
> Oh where shall I find my love?
> Hear my melody,
> Silent, silent, silent.

Smiling, the witch climbed the tree and the dove flew to the prince who was sleeping deeply. She circled around him and sang her song in his dream:

149

Silent, silent, silent,
Trapped in a magic circle,
I became a little white dove,
Oh where shall I find my love?
Hear my melody,
Silent, silent, silent.

Then the prince awoke, but the dove was gone. Something urged him to turn round and hasten back to his bride, fearing she was in danger. When he reached the lake, he was frightened by the strange figure which sat in the branches. She, however, screeched at him: "Why did you stay so long and leave me here alone? The fog has turned my voice hoarse, and my eyes have turned red from the wind, and my skin has shrivelled up and dried with the cold. It is all your fault – quick – get me down, take me to your castle and warm me."

The prince was sad about the change in his bride. Yet, he took the witch by the hand and they went slowly home. At dawn a white dove circled round them, quietly singing. Angrily the witch chased it away, trying to hit it and screaming: "Chase this ugly animal away, I can't stand its song."

But the prince took pity on the little bird. "It may be hungry," said he and took his last loaf of bread and crumbled it onto the path. Straight away the little creature flew down to pick up the crumbs, and the prince gently stroked its head. Then he felt something hard and pulled out a comb. At the same moment the dove vanished and in front of him stood his bride, young and beautiful as she had been before.

The witch, however, was changed into a night bird, which flew screeching behind the poplars and was never seen again.

Then the prince took his beautiful maiden home to his father and the wedding feast was celebrated with pomp and splendour.

From Italy

The Gift of the Holy Man

In a certain country there once lived an extremely poor man. He was so poor that his family went without food most of the time. They did not have enough clothes to cover their bodies, and their home was in a pitiable shape. The poor man was constantly chided by his wife and children for his worthlessness. One day he became tired of his dire poverty and decided that there was nothing left for him to do but wander into the forest and be devoured by wild beasts.

Soon after entering the forest, he came to a house and found a holy man deeply absorbed in meditation nearby. The poor man, out of compassion, swept the courtyard of the mendicant and set his house in order. He also led the holy man's cow to pasture and fed it lush grass. He plucked some wild flowers, and after washing them in pure water, placed them by the praying place of the holy man.

When the holy man finished his meditations he opened his eyes, and the first thing he saw was the poor man. Then he discovered his house was neat and clean, his cow was well fed, and he saw the delicate flowers. Now the holy man was gifted with the power of foreknowledge. He knew immediately that the man standing before him was extremely poor, and he decided to help him.

The holy man asked the poor man to sit by him. The poor man, with great humility, folded his hands and sat by the holy man.

"I know that you are very poor," said the holy man. "But you will not remain poor if you follow my advice. I give you this handkerchief. One side of it is yellow, and the other side is green. If you spread the green side against the ground, you will receive gold coins. Now, take it and do not stop between this forest and your home. If you follow my advice, I am sure that you will never be poor again."

The grateful man salaamed the holy man a hundred times and then set out for his home.

The day was extremely hot, and after he left the shade of the forest the scorching sun soon sapped the poor man's strength. He sat on the steps of a shop to rest. Out of curiosity he spread the green side of the handkerchief against the ground. And lo! A pile of golden coins appeared on the handkerchief.

The shopkeeper saw this wondrous thing happen before his eyes and devised a plan for cheating the poor man out of his wealth. He invited him into his chambers and feasted him with cakes and other sweets. The poor man was amazed and flattered that such hospitality should be offered him.

During the dinner, the shopkeeper cunningly prodded the poor man into disclosing the secret of the handkerchief. The greedy shopkeeper then invited the poor man to spend the night, because he enjoyed so much the company of pious people who were favoured by God.

The poor man accepted right away, and before going to bed, entrusted the handkerchief and gold coins to the shopkeeper. Several times he asked his host to guard the treasure zealously.

The next morning, the poor man prepared to continue his journey home and asked the shopkeeper to return the handkerchief and gold coins.

Imagine what happened! The clever shopkeeper had replaced the magic handkerchief with an ordinary one and now placed it reverently in the poor man's hands, along with the coins. Not suspecting any trickery, the poor man kindly thanked the shopkeeper a hundred times for his generosity and proceeded on his way.

The poor man reached home lightheaded and happy. The first thing he did was to shower the golden coins on his wife's lap. She was elated beyond words. All day long the poor man told the story of the magic handkerchief over and over again. At twilight, he gathered his family together and with a grand flourish spread the handkerchief on the ground. But nothing happened. He spread it again, waited . . . but nothing happened. He rubbed his eyes, laid the handkerchief down again . . . but still, nothing!

The wife thought that she had been brutally deceived, and she stormed and raged at her foolish husband. She accused him of stealing the coins from some rich man's coffers. She grabbed a broom and began beating the poor old man. At last he freed himself from her clutches, and suspecting that the friendly shopkeeper had been the cause of all this trouble, set off in that direction.

As soon as the poor man entered the shop, he accused the shopkeeper of stealing the magic handkerchief.

The shopkeeper pretended that never before in his life had he seen this impertinent man and drove him from the shop.

The poor man tore his hair and cried. Ah, the holy man had warned him not to stop on his way home. If only he had followed the holy man's advice. How could he face him now?

After much indecision, the poor man resolved to go back to the mendicant's house and ask for forgiveness. When he arrived there, he scrubbed the holy man's house and put everything in order. He fed the cow and picked wild flowers for the holy man's praying place.

When the holy man opened his eyes, he said, "Do not worry, I know what has happened to you. You will recover the magic handkerchief."

The next morning the mendicant gave the poor man a thick stick and told him to visit the shopkeeper on his way home. "If you order the stick to beat someone, it will do so until you command it to stop."

The poor man realized that he had been given the magic stick to teach the shopkeeper a good lesson.

After salaaming the mendicant a hundred times, he set off for the shopkeeper's abode. Now the shopkeeper was clever enough to surmise that probably the stick which the poor man carried was magic, too, so he politely received the poor man and apologized for his previous misbehaviour.

The poor man smiled, and feigning innocence, offered to have his magic stick perform. The shopkeeper's wife and children gathered around, and the poor man uttered these words:

"Stick, stick, holy man's stick,
Beat them, beat them hard and quick.
Teach these people that greed is wrong,
Show them right is always strong!"

And see! Wonder of wonders!

The stick began beating the shopkeeper and his family mercilessly. Unable to bear the violent blows, the wife took shelter in her room and the shopkeeper escaped to the roof. But the magic stick was all-knowing and everywhere at once. It doubtlessly would have killed them all had not the shopkeeper fallen prostrate at the poor man's feet and begged forgiveness.

The shopkeeper returned the magic handkerchief and swore a hundred times that he would never again commit such a terrible deed. Now, the poor man, with the magic handkerchief clutched in his hand, proceeded, hastened rather . . . not hastened but rather ran homeward without once stopping.

Reaching home, he shut and locked all the doors, and then spread the handkerchief on the dirt floor as the holy man had instructed. Lo! A pile of gold coins appeared!

He repeated the process just to see if the handkerchief really was genuine, and again a pile of coins appeared. He called his wife and children. They were astonished at seeing the pile of gold coins. The poor man made the handkerchief perform and, of course, from that time on they did not doubt the poor man's word. Within a short time he bought a large estate and passed his days in uninterrupted happiness.

We could end our story here, but unfortunately, life is not like a folktale that ends happily.

The magic power of the handkerchief became known throughout the country. The king heard about the enormous wealth accumulated by the poor man simply by spreading a magic handkerchief on the ground, and he feared that the poor man would soon have more money than he. So the jealous king conceived a plan whereby he could gain possession of the handkerchief.

He sent a chamberlain to the wealthy landlord's estate. We can no longer call the poor man poor, so we shall call him wealthy landlord instead. The chamberlain praised the wealth and piety of the landlord. He also suggested that if the landlord so desired, his eldest son could become the husband of the king's daughter.

Now, to be the father-in-law of a princess was indeed a great honour. The landlord immediately sent a proposal of marriage to the king.

Next day, the chamberlain returned to the landlord and said that the king was pleased with the proposal, but wished to hear it from the lips of the landlord himself. The chamberlain also requested that the magic handkerchief be brought along, because the princess was eager to see its wondrous powers.

The wealthy landlord was received warmly by the king and his court. The king talked politely for a while and then asked if he might take the handkerchief to his daughter. The landlord, without suspecting anything, gave the handkerchief to the king.

Hours passed but no one returned. Finally, the landlord sent a message to the king kindly asking him to return the handkerchief. The king denied that he had ever seen it, and the landlord was driven from the palace. Showing no sign of anger, the landlord quietly went home, got his magic stick and returned to the palace gates, where he uttered these words:

"Stick, stick, holy man's stick,
Beat them, beat them hard and quick,
Teach these people that greed is wrong,
Show them right is always strong!"

The stick began its work. The queen was driven from one corner of her room to the other. The king was forced to crawl under his bed, but, of course, the magic stick followed him and continued its pummelling. The whole court was beaten. Such a scene of disorder was created that words fail to describe it.

Finally, the king, in anguish and pain, fell at the feet of the landlord and begged for mercy. The landlord retrieved his magic handkerchief and went home.

Day by day the landlord's wealth increased. He lived happily to a ripe old age, and one day his eldest son became king of the country.

From Pakistan

The Winning of Kwelanga

Near the Mountains of the Dragon, there once lived a great chief named Ngazulu. He had a daughter who was so beautiful and gentle that she was called Kwelanga, which means surprise.

It was the chief's desire that Kwelanga be married to a man worthy of her. So all suitors were put to impossible tests. Naturally all failed to win her.

One day a young man named Zamo heard about this. At once he decided to try his luck. His father tried to dissuade him. He said, "We are poor people. How dare you think of marrying the daughter of the chief?"

His mother said, "Oh, Zamo! Every man who has tried has lost his life. Do you think you would fare any better?"

But Zamo said, "I can't whistle with another's mouth. I must try it myself."

So one day Zamo went to Chief Ngazulu and said, "Greetings, Nkosi." Then he waited for the chief to speak.

The chief said, "Young man, what are you doing here? Have you lost your way?"

"No, Nkosi," said Zamo, "this is the end of my journey. I have come to propose marriage to your daughter."

"You come, with no attendants, to propose marriage?" cried the chief.

"Nkosi," said Zamo humbly, "it is the custom of my people to act alone."

"Proposer-of-marriage," said the chief, "are you prepared to do the tasks we will set for you?"

"I am here to try," said Zamo.

Ngazulu said, "Well then, look yonder. Do you see that cultivated field? Kaffir corn has been sown there. Before sun down you must gather all the grain that has been scattered. Then you may speak to me of marriage."

At that moment Kwelanga passed by on her way to the stream to draw water. She swayed gracefully beneath the earthen pot balanced on

156

her head. When she saw the handsome suitor talking with her father, she began humming a little tune.

When the young man saw Kwelanga he thought she was as pretty as a sunbird. He said, "Let me begin at once."

Zamo went straight to the field. Finding a huge basket nearby, he took it and began picking up the kernels of kaffir corn. He worked all day without resting. When the sun was about to disappear in the west, he still hadn't finished half the field.

Just then he heard someone singing from the hillside above him:

"Red grains of golden corn
Scattered by our mothers
Fly back from whence you came,
Gather with the others."

Suddenly the basket was heaped with grain. Zamo looked about and saw that the field was clean. He knew that every kernel had returned to the basket, and he carried the grain to Ngazulu.

When the chief saw the filled basket, he said "You did well, young man. But that task was too easy. Tomorrow we shall talk again."

Zamo was given food and a hut in which to sleep. Very early the following morning he went to sit near the chief's door. When Ngazulu came out, he said, "Young man, what do you want with me?"

Zamo said, "Nkosi, I have come to propose marriage at this kraal."

The chief said, "See that forest in the valley? If you are able to chop down all the trees before sunset, then come to me and talk of marriage."

Zamo fetched an axe and went to the forest. He set to work with all speed. Many trees fell before his axe. But the forest was large, and though he worked all day without rest, most of the trees were still left. As the sun was slipping behind the hill, he heard a sweet voice singing:

"Trees of the forest,
In the sun's red glow,
Tall before Zamo –
Bow yourselves low."

157

At that, the trees crashed down on every side. Not one was left standing. Just then the sun set. Zamo went to the chief and said, "Nkosi, have I not finished the task you gave me?"

The chief was very much surprised. He called his counsellor and said, "Think of something really hard for this man to do. The tasks I have given him have been too easy."

The counsellor put his hand over his mouth, as is the way with people in deep thought. Then he said, "Let Zamo come to us in the morning. We will think of something that is not so easy."

The chief and his counsellor sat up all night discussing what trial to give the young man. Just as the sun was rising they came to a decision. When Zamo appeared, the counsellor said, "Young man, do you see that thorn tree growing out from the edge of the cliff – the one way up high on the mountainside? You are to climb out onto it and pluck the topmost thorn."

Zamo saw the scraggly tree growing out from a crag high up on the mountain. No one could climb out on that, he thought. But he said nothing and set off up a steep mountain path.

The chief and his counsellor watched him go. They were sure that Zamo would not be able to climb the tree because of the thorns. Even if he should manage to crawl out onto it, the tree would bend with his weight and surely throw him off into the gorge. In any event, they thought they had seen the last of him.

When Zamo reached the edge of the cliff, he looked down to see what lay beneath the thorn tree. Far, far down he saw nothing but grey rubble – the rocks of all sizes that had rolled down the mountain. He knew that to fall would mean certain death.

The trunk of the thorn tree angled outward and upward from the cliff. Zamo began to creep out onto it, picking his way between big thorns. As he neared the twisted umbrella of branches, the thorns were so close together that there was no place even for his fingertips. Then the tree began to bend. Zamo stopped breathing, and with great difficulty made his way back to the foot of the tree.

Just then he heard a voice singing behind him:

> "Thorn tree, thorn tree,
> Wind and weather worn tree,
> Your topmost thorn, please
> Pluck for Zamo and me."

Suddenly a small grey thorn came twirling through the air. It landed beside Zamo. He picked it up and, turning quickly, he saw Kwelanga coming towards him with outstretched arms. He knew at once that it was she who had sung the magic songs that had helped him every time.

Zamo took Kwelanga's hand, and together they went to her father.

"Nkosi," said Zamo, "here is the topmost thorn. I have finished the tasks. Kwelanga is willing, and I have come to propose marriage at this kraal."

When Ngazulu saw the look of happiness on the face of his daughter, he knew that Zamo truly was worthy of her. For he knew that the best husband for a woman is the man who can make her happy.

A Zulu Tale from Africa, retold by Verna Aardema

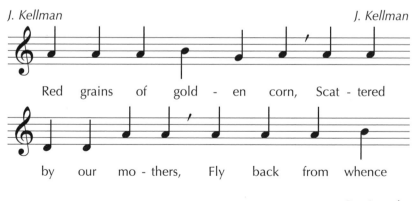

J. Kellman   J. Kellman

Red grains of gold - en corn, Scat - tered

by our mo - thers, Fly back from whence

Continued...

The Magic Horns

Once upon a time there lived a boy whose mother had died. The other women in the compound gave him food to keep him from starving, and they expected him to work hard to repay them for what he ate. And so the boy never had a moment to himself and when night came he was sometimes too tired to sleep.

No sooner had he got back from a long search in the bush for firewood for one woman, than another would shout at him:

"Magoda! Magoda! Go and weed my millet patch and don't come back until it is clear," and off he had to go.

Some hours later he returned, only to be sent off by another woman to search for her son who had not yet returned from the pasture with the goats, and when Magoda finally came back for his supper he often found there was little left for him and he had to go to bed half fed.

As he grew older he became tired of being continually ordered about, and at last he determined to run away. His only possession was an ox which his father had given him and told him to take great care of, so Magoda planned to leave the village one morning before the sun rose while the villagers were still asleep.

The ox seemed to understand the need for silence when Magoda climbed on to his back in the half light, for it stepped delicately out of the compound without cracking a stick with its hooves or flicking the fence with its tail. So Magoda escaped and took to the road, riding on his ox.

As they went along they passed many villages and Magoda could hear the people calling to one another as they set about the day's tasks. He saw women going to the river to get water, while little boys ran along the road behind their flocks of goats and groups of children passed him with big bundles of dry sticks on their heads.

"Aha!" said Magoda to himself. "Never again shall I have to do that kind of work; I'm free! Free! Free!"

But as the day got hotter poor Magoda became hungry and thirsty and wondered how he would be able to get food, now that he had run away from home.

Then suddenly a herd of cattle came along the road with a large bull in the middle of the cows.

Magoda's ox began to speak.

"Get off my back," it said. "Then I can fight that bull."

The boy jumped down, the ox rushed towards the bull, headed it away from the cows and a furious fight began. Soon the bull lay dead and the ox was satisfied.

"There now!" it said to Magoda. "I have proved my strength."

Magoda climbed onto the ox's back again and away they went. By now, the boy was very hungry and as they passed a village where the smoke from the fires rose into the still air, the smell of cooking wafted towards him and Magoda raised his hand in despair.

"What wouldn't I give for some supper!" he exclaimed, and struck the right horn of the ox to emphasize his words.

To his amazement food immediately began to stream out of the horn; beans and maize and meat, all well cooked. Magoda seized it hungrily as it came and stuffed his mouth with all kinds of good things, but even so he could not eat the food quickly enough to prevent some of it falling on the ground.

"This is wonderful! This is splendid!" he said in delight, and smote the animal's left horn with his free hand.

The food stopped coming out of the right horn at once and what had not been eaten was drawn into the other horn, where it disappeared.

"That's the way it is then," said Magoda. "Thank you, good ox! I see that all I have to do is to smite your right horn when I want food and I shall never go hungry."

They jogged along a track together until the sun was setting, when they came upon another herd of cattle. With a deep sigh the ox said to the boy:

"I must take leave of you here. I have to fight this herd, too, but they will kill me. When I am dead you must break off my horns and take them with you. They will provide you with food whenever you need it if you speak to them, but they will not work for anyone else."

"Please don't fight!" begged the boy. "Don't leave me, for you are the only friend I have."

But the ox would not listen. It dashed at the herd and began fighting so fiercely that at first the boy thought his ox would be victorious. Alas, after a time it grew weaker and weaker until it dropped dead.

Sadly Magoda broke off the horns, hid them inside his wrapping cloth and continued his journey. It was now quite dark and he stood still, listening for sounds of a village. Sure enough, away to the west, he heard plaintive singing and the lowing of cattle tied up for the night, so he hurried toward the sounds.

When he reached the village the people were singing a sad song about hunger and the lack of food in their farms, so he knew he would be welcome, provided his horns still gave food now they were no longer attached to a living animal.

"Greetings to you," he called as he reached the village, and with a stick warded off the inquisitive dogs who rushed barking towards him.

"Greetings," replied some of the nearby people. "If it's food and lodging you want, young lad, there's nothing to eat in this hungry spot."

Magoda walked into the centre of the village and sat down in one of the houses at the invitation of a householder and while they were all busy talking he took out the horns and hit one of them hard saying:

"Give me food, oh horn."

Sure enough, the food just flowed out of the horn, like a stream in spate. The people in the house were amazed and began eating at once; then, when they saw that the supply of food seemed endless, they called their friends to come and share in their good fortune. Never had the villagers seen so much food and not one of them went to bed that night with an empty, rumbling stomach.

When they were all filled, Magoda struck the other horn, and the remainder of the food disappeared. Then he, too, lay down and slept soundly, for he had had an exhausting day.

Now the householder who had called Magoda inside and in whose house the horns had displayed their magic power, was a greedy man. He had kept a sharp eye on Magoda and soon discovered that the horns were unusual ones, so he lay down and pretended to sleep, listening all the while for the snores and heavy breathing of the other people in the house. When he was certain they were all sleeping soundly he crept out into the compound and rummaged through the rubbish heaps until he found a couple of ox horns. Then he silently took the magic horns from under Magoda's sleeping-cloth and replaced them with his worthless ones.

The next morning, after bidding the householder and all the villagers' good-bye, Magoda took to the bush again. He did not know where he would go except that he wanted to get as far away as possible from the compound where he had been brought up. About midday he stopped to rest and, of course, spoke to the horns. But nothing happened.

"I expect I struck the left horn instead of the right," he said to himself and reversing the horns he struck the other one and said, again:

"Give me food, oh horn."

But still nothing happened and Magoda was puzzled and depressed. Then he noticed that the horns seemed a little smaller than before and decided that the magic ones must have been stolen and replaced by those he was now holding. There was only one thing to do. He would have to go back to the village where he had slept the previous night and seek out the thief.

He waited until it was almost evening and quietly made his way to the edge of the compound, unnoticed by the bustling crowd of villagers. As it grew dark, he crept up to the house where his horns had provided such a magnificent feast and he almost laughed out loud: for inside he could hear the angry, impatient voice of the householder, saying repeatedly:

"Give me food, oh horn. Give me food! Do you hear me? Give me food, I say!"

Then Magoda remembered that his ox had told him the horns would provide food only when he himself spoke to them. So he waited his chance.

Presently the householder could be heard throwing the horns down on the ground in disgust; then he came stamping out of the doorway and crossed the compound to speak to some of his relatives who were sitting idly round a fire. Quick as lightning Magoda stole into the house, found his magic horns lying by the wall, replaced them with the worthless ones and ran swiftly away.

That night, after a good feast from the horns, Magoda slept in a tree for protection from the wild animals, and as soon as it was light enough to travel he was on his way again, determined to keep his horns well guarded in future.

Presently he came to a fine-looking village where the people seemed more prosperous than those he had met the day before. Walking boldly into the nearest compound he called loudly to the owner, asking if he would allow him to stay there. The owner, a large, ugly man, shouted at him unkindly:

"Go away! We don't want any beggars here. It's difficult enough to feed our own families, let alone worthless, ragged, good-for-nothings like you."

Magoda glanced down at his tattered clothes and decided that he did look more like a beggar than anything else, so he left the compound and made his way to a quiet spot by the river.

"I wonder if these horns would provide me with other things beside food?" he said to himself. "Well, I can but try."

Seizing a horn in one hand he struck it with the other, and said:

"Give me rich clothes, oh horn."

Great was his surprise to see a finely-woven cloth and some beautiful ornaments coming out of the horn. When he put these on he looked like a wealthy man, and decided to go back to the village and try his luck again.

How different was his reception this time! Children stood and stared at him, young men stopped in their tracks to ask him what he wanted and the maidens plying their pestles in their mortars, ceased work and bashfully covered their faces with their hands.

There was one exceptionally beautiful girl, working at the door of her mother's hut, and Magoda made straight for her and asked to speak to her parents. They at once agreed to allow this fine-looking young man to lodge in their home.

Time passed, and Magoda produced food and wealth for all the village and the lovely girl's father gladly gave her to him for a wife. The young couple were able to provide themselves with all they needed by speaking to the horns: a large house, herds of oxen, servants to work in their fields and unlimited food.

So Magoda found happiness at last and he and his wife lived to a grand old age and were blessed with many children.

A Zulu tale from Africa

Akimba and the Magic Cow

Listen, listen and you will hear the sounds and rhythms of the village and the forest. Sounds of nature. The people here still live close to nature. Come, experience with me the magic of the sounds, and see what happens.

Long ago in a little African village, lived a man named Akimba. Akimba was the poorest man in his village. One morning he had nothing left to eat – not even a crumb. "I have no food and I have no money. I must leave the village," Akimba thought, "and see what I can do."

So Akimba set out. Soon he came to a deep forest. He saw an old man chopping firewood. Akimba helped him stack the logs. "Where are you going?" the old man asked. "I have no food and I have no money. I must see what I can do," Akimba said. "Maybe I can help you," said the old man. "Behind this bush you'll find a cow. Take her home with you and say 'kukuku.' Say 'kukuku' to her and see what happens."

So Akimba took the cow and went back to his hut. "Kukuku," he said to her. The cow opened her mouth and a gold coin fell out. "Wah!" cried Akimba. "Kukuku! Kukuku!" And in no time at all, Akimba was rich.

One day Akimba had to go on a long journey. He could not take his cow with him. So he went to see his good neighbour Bumba. "Bumba," he said, "will you keep my cow for me? She's no trouble as long as you don't say 'kukuku' to her. 'Kukuku' is the one thing you must never say." – "Very well," Bumba said. "I will do as you wish."

So Akimba gave Bumba the cow and went down the road. The very moment Akimba was gone, Bumba ran up to the cow. "Kukuku," he said. To his amazement the cow opened her mouth and a gold coin fell out. "Kukuku," Bumba said again. Another coin fell to the ground. "Wah!" cried Bumba. "This cow is good to have and better to keep."

A few days later, Akimba came back. "Where is my cow?" he asked. "Here she is," Bumba said. But he gave Akimba another cow instead.

Akimba took the cow home and said, "Kukuku." – "Moo-oo," said the cow, but nothing happened. "Have you forgotten your master's voice?" Akimba shouted. "Kukuku, kukuku!" – "Moo-oo, moooo-oooo," mooed the cow. But no gold coins came.

So Akimba went to find the old man in the woods. "My cow stopped giving gold," Akimba said. "Soon I will be hungry again." – "Behind this bush you'll find a sheep. Take her home with you and say 'bururu.' Say 'bururu' to her and see what happens."

So Akimba took the sheep and went back to his hut. "Bururu," he said to her. The sheep opened her mouth and a silver coin fell out. "Wah!" Akimba shouted. "Bururu, bururu!" And in no time at all, Akimba was rich.

But the day came when Akimba had to leave on another journey. He brought his sheep to his good neighbour Bumba. "Bumba," he asked, "will you keep my sheep for me? She's no trouble as long as you don't say 'bururu' to her. 'Bururu' is the one thing you must never say." – "Very well," Bumba said. "I will do as you wish."

The moment Akimba was gone, Bumba ran to the sheep. "Bururu!" he said. The sheep opened her mouth. A silver coin fell out. "Wah!" Bumba shouted. "This sheep is good to have and better yet to keep."

A few weeks later, Akimba came back. "Where is my sheep?" he asked. "Here she is," said Bumba. But he gave Akimba another sheep instead.

Akimba hurried home. "Bururu," he said to the sheep. "Baa, baa," said the sheep. But no silver coins fell out. "Bururu, bururu!" Akimba shouted. Still no silver coins! "This sheep has turned deaf in my absence," said Akimba. And he went to find the old man in the woods.

"My sheep stopped giving silver," Akimba said. "Soon I'll be as hungry as before." – "There is a chicken behind this bush. Take her with you," said the old man. "When you get home, say 'klaklakla' to her. Say 'klaklakla' and see what happens."

So Akimba got the chicken and took her home. "Klaklakla," he said to her. The chicken laid an egg. "What?" yelled Akimba. "No silver? No gold? Klaklakla," he shouted. The chicken laid more eggs. "Well," said Akimba, "eggs are eggs." And he ate them.

The next time he was called away, he asked Bumba to keep his chicken. "She's no trouble as long as you don't say 'klaklakla' to her. 'Klaklakla' is the one thing you must never say." – "Do not worry," Bumba said. "I will be more than glad to keep your chicken."

As soon as Akimba was out of sight, Bumba ran to the chicken. "Klaklakla!" he shouted. The chicken laid an egg. "Fooh!" cried Bumba. "No gold? No silver? Only eggs? Oh well," he thought, "eggs are eggs." And he ate them.

And when Akimba came back and asked for his chicken, Bumba gave him another one instead.

So Akimba went to see the old man in the woods again. "My cow stopped giving gold," he cried. "My sheep stopped giving silver. Even my chicken stopped laying eggs. Soon I will be as hungry as before." – "There's a stick behind the bush," the old man said. "Go home and tell it to dance for you. When you want it to stop say 'mulu.'" – "Thank you," said Akimba, and he took the stick.

As soon as he was home, he told the stick to dance. But the stick did not dance. It jumped up and beat him instead. Akimba was so surprised he almost forgot the magic word. "Mulu!" he yelled at last, and the stick fell to the floor. Akimba looked at the stick for a long time. "Hmmm," he thought "I must pay another visit to Bumba." Then Akimba took the stick to Bumba's house.

"Bumba," he said, "I have to leave again. Will you keep the stick for me?" – 'Well, well,' Bumba thought, 'the cow brought me gold, the sheep brought me silver and the chicken brought me eggs. Who knows what the stick will bring?' And he grabbed the stick and pushed Akimba out of the door. Akimba turned around. "I almost forgot," he said. "Do not say 'Stick, dance for me'. Remember, whatever you do, do not ask the stick to dance."

The moment Akimba was out of sight Bumba yelled, "Stick, dance for me!" And the stick jumped up. But it did not dance. It beat him and beat him and would not stop. The stick was still beating Bumba when Akimba came back. "Now will you give me my true cow and my true sheep and my true chicken?" Akimba asked.

"Anything!" cried Bumba. "Just stop this stick from beating me!" – "Mulu," Akimba said. And the stick fell to the floor.

Akimba picked up the stick. He took his true cow, his true sheep and his true chicken. Then he went back to his hut. "Klaklakla," he said to his chicken. Akimba's plate was filled with eggs. "Bururu," he said to the sheep. And silver coins clanked to the floor. "Kukuku," he said to his cow. And gold coins piled up to the roof.

Akimba never had to go hungry again.

A folk tale from Africa, retold by Ann Rose

The Story of the Shining Princess

Far up in the mountains, nestling in a cool green valley, stood a most beautiful kraal. The hut was a bright green, for it was finely thatched with grass, and the floor within was of the firmest and most brilliantly polished red earth. Around the inner walls stood the cooking pots made of red clay, and along with these were shining green calabashes overflowing with the richest milk and cream. On part of the floor lay fine green mats, but on another part lay the prettiest one of all, woven of gold-coloured grass. Encircling the hut itself was a high green fence, a work of beauty, too; indeed, everything was in perfect order and no other kraal in the countryside could claim to be its equal.

This was the home of a great Chief's wife. The Chief, who had been dead for many years, had left his Queen alone in the world with only one little daughter named Maholia, who was three years old when he died. His Queen had once been a most beautiful woman, and as the little girl grew up, she became just as lovely as her mother. The greatest care was taken in rearing her, and she soon became as good and obedient as she was charming.

The Queen had not married again, for in her tribe this did not befit a king's wife, and so she lived only for the child, Maholia, and they loved one another dearly. Maholia was the envy of every little girl in the country, because everything she wore was the colour of the golden moon: her necklaces, her bracelets, and the gold band that she wore around her neck. As she grew up, she became more and more celebrated for her beauty and charm; in fact she was so lovely that she dazzled the eyes of all who beheld her, and she became known among her people as the Shining Princess.

Time went on, and as she grew into womanhood, many, many suitors came forth to ask for her hand in marriage. There was not a chief's son in that part of the country who did not long to make her his wife. But neither the Princess herself nor her mother was enamoured of any of the men who presented themselves, and so they waited for the right one to appear.

Then one day, an ambassador, a chief Induna, from a very powerful King arrived in the kraal. He had searched in many places for a beautiful maiden to become the wife of the King's son. But though he had travelled far and wide and brought many girls back to his King's kraal, not one had suited the old Chief. And so the King had sent the chief Induna out yet again, to yet more distant lands, to inspect all the Princesses who were famous for their beauty. Now after many months of travelling, with no success, the Induna had come to see the Shining Princess. He had heard talk of her and thought it wise to seek her out, though he secretly feared that he would meet with disappointment once again.

At the sight of the green kraal, the hopes of the ambassador rose. They soared even higher when the Princess came to the door to greet him, for there she stood, her blackness glistening from head to foot in the bright sunlight. Round her neck were thick bars of red-gold copper. Adorning her shapely arms from wrist to elbow were copper and brass rings, and these appeared also on her slender ankles and reached almost to her knees. A girdle of golden beads encircled her waist, and its long glistening fringes hung over her short apron of skin. Over her pretty shoulders hung her cloak, embroidered in circles of gold and bordered with a wide band of shining beads. Even her snuff-calabash was of gold coloured jackalskin. All of her movements were full of grace, and her laughing lips and bright eyes were a sign of the kindness in her heart.

When the Induna saw this beautiful woman, clad in gold and shining like the rising moon, he rejoiced and said, "This is indeed the Princess that I have been searching for! There is no doubt that this is the true wife for our great King's son!"

He begged to see Maholia's mother and formally demanded the hand of her daughter. But many days passed in discussion, since the Queen was not anxious to part with her only child. The Induna, however, spoke so well of his master's power and riches, and so eloquently of the bravery and wisdom of the bridegroom, that at last she consented to the union. The ambassador could now return to his home with the joyous news for his King.

Upon his arrival, the King listened to the description of Maholia and then heaped great praise on the Induna for his selection of such a maiden. While the Induna rested, the King gathered together the marriage gift of cattle for Maholia's mother. This consisted of one hundred beautiful animals, at the head of which marched a fairy ox, a beast who was truly magnificent. He was as black as charcoal, save for two long white horns, and between his shoulders burned a steady light, which illumined his path at night and gave him magic powers. This beast was the King's great pride, but he was considered due payment for so fair a Princess as Maholia.

When all was ready, the wedding party started out to fetch the bride and at the same time to deliver the marriage gift to her mother. The Queen was delighted with the cattle and especially with the fairy ox who led them. Upon receiving him, she took him directly to her daughter. "Here," she said to her child, "take this ox with you. He is my present to you; your journey will be a long one, and you will be happy to ride him when you are tired."

Then turning to the King's men, she warned them, "Do not leave my daughter alone on your return journey. I am afraid of what can happen to her. If you should leave her, I shall know that at once, for the corner of our hut where she always sat will crumble away."

Of course the wedding party promised faithfully to guard Maholia with the greatest care. And feeling reassured, the Princess and her mother parted with both tears of joy and tears of sadness. Thus Maholia and her attending maidens set forth upon their journey with the King's men.

For two days all went well. But on the third day the men came upon hundreds of deer of every kind, and behind these appeared great herds of elephants and giraffes. In short the country was abundant with game, and the King's men were not able to resist such overwhelming temptation. Off they went to hunt, with even the maidens joining the party, all in pursuit of the fleeing animals. Only the Shining Princess stayed behind, with the fairy ox close by her side. At that very moment, as her mother sat in the hut anxiously thinking of her daughter, the corner on which the golden mat had lain, cracked from end to end and crumbled away. And the Queen knew that Maholia was in danger.

In the meantime the wedding party went on with the hunt; and the further they went, the more animals appeared. The hunters forgot all about the poor bride and continued their chase for many days, while she sat alone. Finally it was her misfortune to be discovered by a group of cannibals, who seized her with ease and carried her off. Luckily their attempt to capture the fairy ox failed; he managed to escape them with one great leap into the air, and then he flew like the wind to the hut of the Princess's mother.

The poor Queen was there to meet him at the gate of the kraal, for she knew some evil had befallen her daughter. She knelt before the great ox, while he stood and related his tale.

"But where is Maholia now?" cried the Queen. "Where have they taken her?"

"I know nothing else," replied the ox. "As soon as the cannibals took her, I came to you with all possible speed. Please do not despair; all will turn out well!"

In the meantime the King and his son waited and waited for the expected bride. Weeks and months passed by, and they began to fear that some great calamity had overtaken the party. Then, one by one their men straggled in to tell their shameful tale, that they had left the Princess all alone and forgotten all about her. They had finally returned to the place where they had left her, but she was nowhere to be found, though they had searched the forest far and wide. The King was furious and had all the men put to death; and then calling his wise men together, he asked them for their advice. How could the Princess be found? The wise men decided that the bridegroom, himself, must go with a group of select men to search for the bride, starting at her mother's home.

The anguished Queen received the party with much joy, but her joy became complete despair when she learned that they knew nothing of her daughter. When they questioned her, she told them of the return of the fairy ox and the story that he had brought her.

"Please, Queen Mother, be of good cheer," begged the Prince. "I, myself, will take the fairy ox and together we will search for your daughter. I promise you that I shall never return until I can bring her back with me."

Having uttered these words, the Prince tarried no longer. Taking the fairy ox, he set forth upon his journey. He travelled for weeks and months, but not one trace of the Princess did he discover, until the day that he came upon a marula tree, covered with shining yellow fruit.

This would be just the fruit to make excellent cider, he thought as he smelled the sweet fragrance of the fruit. I must taste it.

He had eaten but a few berries when a deep voice came out of the tree.

"What do you want?" it demanded to know.

"I am in search of the Shining Princess," retorted the Prince. "Can I be assured that I am following the right course?"

"Keep going forward," advised the marula tree, "until you come to the big fig tree."

And so the Prince journeyed further, through country overgrown with bush, until he came to an immense tree covered with little red figs. The figs were so numerous that they even grew on the roots, and the leaves were so thick that no sunlight could pierce them. Sitting down to rest in the tree's deep shade, the Prince said, "I seek the Shining Princess. Am I going the right way?"

"Oh, yes," answered the fig tree, "go on until you come to a big river. Beyond it lies a great forest and in that forest you will find the Princess." The Prince jumped up, filled with renewed hope, and ran along the course of the stream. On the next day he found himself in full view of a deep river; but it was so flooded and swollen, he could not hope to cross it.

"Climb on my back," said the fairy ox, who was the faithful companion of the Prince. "I will carry you across the river."

The Prince was happy to do just that, and the ox plunged into the water, swimming across with no difficulty and then racing over a huge plain beyond. In the far distance the forest was soon visible, and it appeared to grow larger every hour, until finally the two were within its borders. The trees there were taller and thicker than any the Prince had ever seen, and their branches were completely entwined at their peaks. No path at all was visible to the eye, for only the dimmest light filtered through to the forest floor.

The Prince was forced to wander through the thick growth, groping for hours in a land without sun, without one open glade. Then at last, in the distance, he seemed to detect a shining pool of water; and guided only by this distant shimmer, he plunged forward. Drawing nearer, he could see that the pool was surrounded by reeds, the tallest of which stood in the centre. The gleam of the water grew brighter and more golden, until at the end, as he burst through the thicket, he found that this was no pool at all, but rather the Shining Princess herself, seated in a circle of tall grasses.

The Prince hailed her with delight and thanksgiving, for never had he hoped to find such a beauty as she. Maholia, on her part, welcomed him warmly and soon told him how she had been taken through this very forest by the cannibals who had captured her. Luckily, she had managed to escape from them one dark night, as they attempted to bring her to their King. And ever since then she had been living in the midst of the great bush. After the Princess had told of her adventures, the Prince had to tell of his, ending his account by telling Maholia how beautiful she was and how she was worth every danger he had encountered. This was her favourite part of his story, and she wanted to hear it over and over again. Thus they sat for hours among the ferns, telling one another of their wanderings and of their love for each other.

Indeed, they might never have left the forest, had not the Princess suddenly remembered her mother and the deep anguish that she must be suffering.

"But how will I be able to get you home?" asked the Prince, "Everyone will envy me such a beautiful woman, and they will try to steal you away from me. If only it were possible to hide you."

"I can help you!" exclaimed the fairy ox, nuzzling the bride affectionately. "I will turn the Princess into an ugly old man for now, and then no one will trouble us."

So for the time being, Maholia became a little old man, and she mounted the fairy ox with her beloved Prince beside her. Together they all flew over forest, river and mountain; and at the end of seven days, they reached the home of Maholia's mother.

Then at last, all was safely ended. For the Shining Princess became a dazzling bride, and she and her husband set out for their own kingdom. There they reigned in great peace and happiness, with the fairy ox remaining as their devoted follower and adviser for the rest of his days.

A Msuto Story from Africa retold by Terry Berger

The Arrow Chain

There were once two boys, a chief's son and his best friend, who lived together in the same village and always played together. They spent their days making arrows out of feathers and birch twigs, and walking in the countryside around their village.

One summer night, they set out for their playing fields and walked across a large, grassy field. The moon was full and very bright, and almost seemed to be watching them.

"Look at the moon," said the friend, laughing. "How silly and ugly it looks with all those marks all over its face!"

"Hush," whispered the chief's son. "You mustn't say things like that about the moon!"

As soon as he had spoken, a huge shadow swept over the field, and a strange, shimmering rainbow appeared out of the shadow and settled around his friend. When it disappeared, his friend was gone.

He called and called to him, but there was no answer. "The moon has taken him," he thought, and sat down on the hillside and cried. When he had no more tears, he looked up at the sky and saw a large, bright star beside the moon. "I am going to aim for that star," he thought. He took out his bow and arrow, and aiming very carefully, he shot at the star. In a moment the star disappeared, and the arrow did not return. Encouraged, he pulled out another arrow and over and over again, he shot in the same direction, at the place where the star had been. He used nearly all of the arrows that he and his friend had made.

When almost all the arrows were gone, he looked up and saw something hanging from the sky, very close to him; it was a chain of arrows, one fastened to the other. He shot a few more, until the chain almost reached the ground. Just as he shot the last arrow, the sun began to rise. As its first rays touched the chain of arrows, it became a ladder, leading up to the sky.

The chief's son decided to climb up. First, he took some berry bush branches and stuck them into his hair. He climbed and climbed all day and camped on the ladder at nightfall. In the morning when he awoke his head felt heavy – he pulled out the branches and they were filled with ripe berries. He ate and ate, felt strengthened and continued climbing.

By the time he reached the top, he was very tired. He looked around and saw a large lake and lay down beside it and fell asleep. In his sleep he heard a small voice speaking to him, saying, "Wake up, I am coming for you." He opened his eyes and saw a little girl standing beside him.

"I have come to take you to my grandmother," said the girl. "She has been watching you climb up from earth." And so the chief's son followed the little girl through the sky country until they came to the grandmother's house. The old woman welcomed them. "You are brave to come up here to the sky country," she said. "What do you seek here?" – "I have come to find my friend," answered the chief's son.

"Yes, I know," said the old woman. "First you must have food, for you are weak from hunger." She raised her hand to her mouth, and a roasted fish appeared upon it. She raised it again, and there was a toasted ear of corn. A third time she raised it, and it was laden with fresh fruit. The chief's son ate hungrily, and soon felt strong and refreshed.

"Now," said the grandmother, "when you go to the house of the moon, you must take four things." She handed him a pine cone, a fish eye, a rose and a small piece of stone. Then she and the girl wished him good luck and stood at the door of their house as he hurried away into the land of the moon.

He could hear his friend crying from high up and saw his head sticking out of the smoke hole. He climbed up onto the roof, stepping softly so that the moon could not hear him. His friend was so glad to see him that he stopped crying. "Don't stop!" the chief's son whispered. "The moon mustn't know I am taking you away!" So his friend cried on as he was pulled out of the smoke hole. He pushed the pine cone into his place, and it began to wail just as his friend had done. Then, hand in hand, they jumped down from the roof and started to run.

But soon the pine cone fell into the fire and stopped wailing. The moon realized he had been tricked and set off after them, much faster

S. Howard

S. Howard

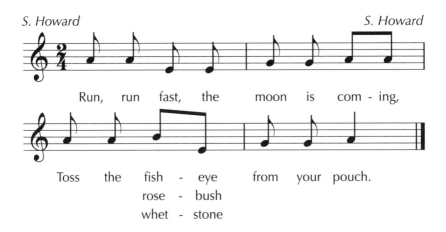

Run, run fast, the moon is com - ing,

Toss the fish - eye from your pouch.
rose - bush
whet - stone

than they could run.

The chief's son tossed the fish eye behind him, and where it fell a large lake appeared. The moon fell into the water and had to crawl out and roll all the way around the lake after them.

Repeat song.

The chief's son then tossed the rose behind him. A rosebush appeared and caught the moon in its thorns. Slowly the moon struggled free and soon he was close behind them again.

Repeat song.

The chief's son tossed the little stone behind him and a giant mountain appeared. It was so steep that the moon could not climb it, but kept rolling back down, again and again.

At last the two friends reached the grandmother's house. They were very glad to be together again. They thanked her for all the help she had given them and said they longed to be back on the earth again. The grandmother said, "You may return to the earth whenever you wish."

Bidding the old woman goodbye, the two friends walked across the sky country until they came to the top of the ladder. There they lay down, longing to be back home again, and fell asleep. When they awoke, they found themselves back home again on the hillside. They were greeted with cries of joy by their friends and families from the village. They led long and happy lives. And people came from all around to hear their wonderful story.

A Tlingit tale, adapted by Susan Howard for use as a marionette play

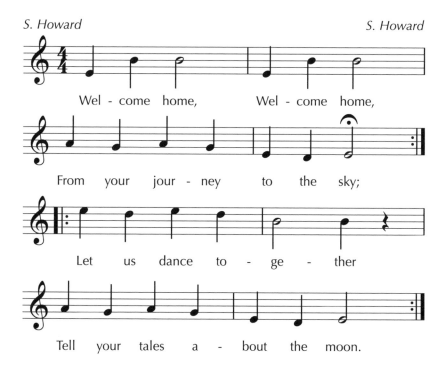

The Two Brothers

Early one morning two brothers left their village and went out into the bush to hunt. They each carried a bow and some arrows and wore a big leather bag slung over one shoulder, which they hoped would be full of meat when they returned.

For a long time they trudged along the sandy paths that led away from the village out into the wild bush, and as they walked a snake would sometimes go slithering into the long grass in front of their feet or a bush-fowl would rise suddenly into the air, squawking with fear.

Presently, they left the path behind and had to make their way across a country full of boulders and thorn bushes, a place where only hunters and travellers penetrated.

Suddenly, they came across a row of red clay cooking-pots standing upside down.

"What's this?" said the younger son. "Who can have left these pots in a deserted place like this?"

"Do not touch them," begged the older son. "I don't like the look of them. There's magic about and we'd best leave them alone."

But the younger son had always been the braver of the two and he refused to pass on as his older brother suggested.

"I'm going to look underneath the pots, whatever you say," he said, and as he bent down to put the pots the right way up, his brother ran a little distance away and stood watching him anxiously.

The boy turned over the first pot and found nothing underneath, and then he did the same to each pot along the line. There seemed no magic about any of them, but as he turned over the last pot he gave a shout of surprise, for out popped a little old woman.

She took no notice of the younger boy, neither did she thank him for letting her out, but turning to the older lad she shouted:

"Don't stand shivering over there like a frightened gazelle. I won't hurt you. Now follow me and I will show you something worth seeing."

But the boy was still terrified and would not take even one step towards her.

"Coward!" she exclaimed. Then she turned to the younger boy and commanded him to go with her. He was always ready for an adventure and went at once.

He followed her for some time until suddenly she stopped in front of a big tree. Handing the boy an axe, she said:

"Cut this tree down for me."

At the first stroke of the axe, a bullock stepped out of the tree-trunk, and each time the boy chopped at the tree a cow, a bullock, a goat or a sheep came out, until at last he was surrounded by flocks and herds.

"These are for you," said the woman. "Now drive them all back to your home. I shall stay here."

The boy was almost too amazed to speak, but he remembered his manners sufficiently to thank the old woman.

Driving all the animals before him, he soon came back to the place where he had left his elder brother.

"Just look at what the old woman gave me!" exclaimed the boy happily. "Don't you wish that you had followed her when she called you?"

He told his brother all that had happened, and together they began to drive the flocks and herds back towards their village.

The grass was scorched and brown, for it was the middle of the dry season, and both the boys were very thirsty – while the animals cried loudly from time to time, as they nosed unsuccessfully for food on the parched ground.

A little further on, as they were passing along the edge of a steep precipice, the older boy, peering over the edge, suddenly gave a shout.

"Look! Water!" he exclaimed, pointing down to where the sparkle of a small stream could be seen among the trees and grasses. "If you tie a rope round me and lower me over the precipice, I can drink my fill."

The younger brother did as he was asked, and soon the older one came up from the stream again, refreshed and cheerful.

"Now let me down on the rope," said the younger brother, and slowly the older boy let out the rope so that his brother could quench his thirst too.

Suddenly an evil thought came to the elder boy. He knew that there was no way to climb up from the valley and with a flick of his hand he threw the rope over the edge, turned round, and began driving the animals home, leaving his brother to perish at the foot of the precipice.

The journey home was slow and tiring, but when the older boy arrived and was greeted in surprise by his parents, he lied to them.

"An old woman gave these animals to me," he said.

"But where is your brother?" they asked.

"Has he not yet returned? He grew tired of our journey and said he would go home again. I have not seen him since midday," replied the boy.

Of course the younger brother did not come back that night, but the parents were not unduly worried as they thought he had changed his mind and gone hunting in another direction after all.

Early the next morning, while the women of the village were getting water at the well, they heard the song of a honey-bird. There were many of these birds in that part of Africa and people had discovered that if they followed a singing honey-bird, it generally led them to a bees' nest where the men could gather honey.

So, hurrying back to their husbands, the women called out:

"Quick! We hear a honey-bird. Follow it and get us some honey."

Several men, including the father of the boy who was still missing, ran to the place where the bird was singing, and waited for it to begin to fly.

Off it went, followed by the men, who became more and more surprised at the distance the bird was flying. Through the bush they ran, pausing only when the bird rested on a tree for a few moments, then on again through the thick undergrowth until the men scarcely knew where they were.

At last one of them called to the others:

"I've gone far enough. I don't believe this bird is leading us to honey, and I am getting so weary that I think I'll turn back."

At this, the bird sang and chirped so much louder than before, and fluttered its wings so violently, that the men were puzzled.

"It almost seems as though the bird wants us to go on," said the father of the two boys. "Let us go just a little further."

So on they went, until at last they came to a precipice and from far down below a faint voice reached them, calling for help. The bird flew up and down excitedly, then swooped into the valley and landed at the feet of the boy.

The father leant over the edge and strained his eyes to see where the bird had gone.

"My son!" he exclaimed. "I do believe that is my son."

Quickly the men fashioned a rope from nearby creepers, and very soon they hauled the boy up the precipice, when he told them the whole story of his adventures.

"Alas," wept the father, "that I should have a son so wicked as your older brother. You would have died had not the magic honey-bird led us to this place."

"The older boy must be punished," said the men angrily. "It was only his greed that made him leave his brother here, pretending that the cattle were his own."

But news of the younger son's rescue must have reached home before the men, since the older brother had already disappeared when they returned and he never came back to the village again.

But the younger boy prospered as his flocks and herds increased and his parents wanted for nothing in their old age.

A Zulu tale from Africa

The Grateful Statues

Once upon a time an old man and an old woman were living in a country village in Japan. They were very poor and spent every day weaving big hats out of straw. Whenever they finished a number of hats, the old man would take them to the nearest town to sell them.

One day the old man said to the old woman: "New Year is the day after tomorrow. How I wish we had some rice-cakes to eat on New Year's Day! Even one or two little cakes would be enough. Without some rice-cakes we can't even celebrate New Year's Day."

"Well, then," said the old woman, "after you've sold these hats, why don't you buy some rice-cakes and bring them back with you?"

So early the next morning the old man took the five new hats that they had made, and went to town to sell them. But after he got to town he was unable to sell a single hat. And to make things still worse, it began to snow very hard.

The old man was sad as he began trudging wearily back toward his village. He was going along a lonesome mountain trail when he suddenly came upon a row of six stone statues of Jizo, the protector of children, all covered with snow.

"My, my! Now isn't this a pity," the old man said. "These are only stone statues of Jizo, but even so, just think how cold they must be standing here in the snow."

"I know what I'll do!" the old man suddenly said to himself. "This will be just the thing."

So he unfastened the five new hats from his back and began tying them, one by one, on the heads of the Jizo statues.

When he came to the last statue he suddenly realized that all the hats were gone. "Oh, my!" he said, "I don't have enough hats." But then he remembered his own hat. So he took it off his head and tied it on the head of the last Jizo. Then he went on his way home.

When he reached his house the old woman was waiting for him by the fire. She took one look at him and cried: "You must be frozen half to

186

death. Quick! Come to the fire. What did you do with your hat?"

The old man shook the snow out of his hair and came to the fire. He told the old woman how he had given all the new hats, and even his own hat, to the six stone Jizo. He told her he was sorry that he hadn't been able to bring any rice-cakes.

"My! That was a very kind thing you did for the Jizo," said the old woman. She was very proud of the old man, and went on: "It's better to do a kind thing like that than to have all the rice-cakes in the world. We'll get along without any rice-cakes for New Year's Day."

By this time it was late at night, so the old man and woman went to bed. Just before dawn, while they were still asleep, a very wonderful thing happened. Suddenly there was the sound of voices in the distance, singing:

"A kind old man walking in the snow
Gave all his hats to the stone Jizo.
So we bring him gifts with a yo-heave-ho!"

The voices came nearer and nearer, and then you could hear the sound of footsteps on the snow.

The sounds came right up to the house where the old man and woman were sleeping. And then all at once there was a great noise, as though something had been put down just in front of the house.

The old couple jumped out of bed and ran to the front door. When they opened it, what do you suppose they found? Well, right there at the door someone had spread a straw mat, and arranged very neatly on the mat was one of the biggest and most beautiful and freshest rice-cakes the old people had ever seen.

"Whoever could have brought us such a wonderful gift?" they said, and looked about wonderingly.

They saw some tracks in the snow leading away from their house. The snow was all tinted with the colours of dawn, and there in the distance, walking over the snow, were the six stone Jizo, still wearing the hats which the old man had given them.

The old man said: "It was the stone Jizo who brought this wonderful rice-cake to us."

The old woman said: "You did them a kind favour when you gave them your hats, so they brought this rice-cake to show their gratitude."

The old couple had a very wonderful New Year's Day celebration after all, because now they had this wonderful rice-cake to eat.

From Japan

The Bamboo Maiden

Once there was an old man who used to play on a bamboo flute every day. To his surprise the flute began to soften, and at last it became a lovely maiden. The old man said, "Beautiful spirit of the flute, will you remain here as my daughter?"

The maiden smiled and said, "It was your love of music that caused me to come to earth." And she remained as his daughter, and he loved her very much.

Now, the maiden was so beautiful, so gentle, and so loving to her old father, that she became known all over the Empire. Many men sought her as their bride, but she told her father she did not want to marry.

One day five young men came to ask the old man for the maiden. When he told her, she said, "I will marry the one who can obtain three things for me: a silver pin four inches long; a branch from the cassia tree in the moon; and a key of gold from the Yellow Sea.

When the young men heard this, they set out to get the silver pin, the branch of the cassia tree, and the key of gold from the Yellow Sea.

The first youth had no patience. He soon gave up and returned to his home.

The second one had a silver pin and a golden key made. Then he broke off a branch of a cassia tree. But when the maiden saw these things, she said, "This cassia branch is of earth." So the dishonest man went away and never returned.

The third youth searched and searched for the three precious things, but at last he became ill and died.

The fourth youth went into an official's house and tried to steal the treasures. He was put in prison and never returned to the home of the bamboo maiden.

Now, as the fifth youth went toward the Yellow Sea, he came upon a wild goose who fluttered helplessly upon the ground. The youth was filled with pity and asked: "Wild goose, why do you flutter about upon the earth? Why don't you fly up into the heavens?"

The wild goose replied, "Youth with the Heart of Kindness, I cannot move one of my wings. I am always in pain."

The youth looked at the wing of the wild goose and found that some one had fastened the wing together with a silver pin. When he removed it, the wild goose said, "Youth with the Heart of Kindness, allow me to give you this silver pin." Then the goose flew up into the heavens, and the youth went his way filled with happiness.

As he approached the Yellow Sea, he saw a poor old man sitting upon the ground. "Give me a little money! I have had no food for days and days," cried the old man.

The youth was moved by the suffering face of the old man, and gave him his purse and all of his money.

The old man said. "Youth with the Heart of Kindness, I shall keep the money, but here is the purse."

The youth took it, and lo, it suddenly changed into the branch of a cassia tree. Then he went his way with a heart full of happiness.

As he walked along the beach of the Yellow Sea he saw a fish that lay gasping upon the sand. Filled with pity, the youth picked up the fish and put it back into the water.

Immediately it darted down into the sea, then returned to him with a golden key in its mouth. With a low bow, the fish placed the key at the feet of the youth.

Here were the three precious things! With his heart nearly bursting with happiness, he hastened back to the home of the old man.

Then the Bamboo Maiden married the Youth with the Heart of Kindness. They lived happily, and had many sons and daughters.

From China

The Sticky-Sticky Pine

Once there was a woodcutter. He was very poor but very kind. Never would he tear off the living branches of a tree to make firewood. Instead, he would gather only the dead branches on the ground. He knew what happened when you tore a branch off a tree. The sap, which is the blood of a tree, would drip and drip, just as though the poor tree were bleeding. So, since he didn't want to harm the trees, he never tore off the branches.

One day he was walking beneath a high pine tree hunting for firewood when he heard a voice, saying:

"Sticky, sticky is my sap,
For my tender twigs are snapped."

The woodcutter looked and, sure enough, someone had broken tree limbs off the pine and the sap was running out. Skillfully, he mended them, saying:

"Now these tender twigs I'll wrap,
And in that way stop the sap."

And he tore a piece from his own clothes to make a bandage.

No sooner had he finished than many tiny gold and silver things fell from the tree. It was money – a lot of it. The surprised woodcutter was almost covered up with it. He looked at the tree and smiled and thanked it. Then he took the money home.

There was a great amount and he slowly realized that he was now a very rich woodcutter indeed. Everyone knows that the pine tree is the sign of prosperity in Japan and, sure enough, the grateful pine had made him very rich.

Just then a face appeared in the window. It was the face of another woodcutter. But this woodcutter was neither nice nor kind. In fact, it was he who had torn off the branches of the pine and had broken its twigs. When he saw the money he said: "Where did you get all that money? Look how nice and bright it is."

The good woodcutter held up the money so the other could see. It was oblong in shape, the way money used to be in Japan, and he had five basketfuls. He told the bad woodcutter how he had got the money.

"From that big pine tree?"

"Yes, that was the one."

"Hmm," said the bad woodcutter, and ran away as fast as he could go. He ran right up to the old pine tree, and the tree said:

> "Sticky, sticky, is my blood.
> Touch me, you'll receive a flood."

"Oh, just what I want," said the bad man, "a flood of gold and silver." He reached up and broke off another branch. The pine tree suddenly showered him. But it showered him with sticky, sticky sap – not gold and silver at all.

The bad woodcutter was covered with sap. It got in his hair and on his arms and legs. Since it was so sticky, he couldn't move and though he called for help, no one could hear him. He had to remain there for three days – one day for each branch – until the sap became soft enough for him to drag himself home.

And, after that, he never broke another branch off a living tree.

From Japan

The Spider Weaver

Long ago there was a farmer named Yosaku. One day he was working in the fields and saw a snake getting ready to eat a spider. Yosaku felt sorry for the spider. So he ran at the snake with his hoe and drove the snake away. Then the spider disappeared into the grass, but first it seemed to pause a minute and bow in thanks towards Yosaku.

One morning not long after that, Yosaku was in his house when he heard a tiny voice outside calling: "Mr. Yosaku, Mr. Yosaku." He went to the door and saw a beautiful young girl standing in the yard.

"I heard that you are looking for someone to weave cloth for you," said the girl. "Won't you please let me live here and weave for you?"

Yosaku was pleased because he did need a weaving girl. So he showed the girl the weaving room and she started to work at the loom. At the end of the day Yosaku went to see what she'd done and was surprised to find that she'd woven eight long pieces of cloth, enough to make eight kimono. He'd never known anyone who could weave so much in just a single day.

"How ever did you weave so much?" he asked the girl.

But instead of answering him, she said: "You mustn't ask me that. And you must never come into the weaving room while I am at work."

But Yosaku was curious. So one day he slipped quietly up to the weaving room and peeped in the window. What he saw surprised him! Because it was not the girl who was seated at the loom, but a large spider, weaving very fast with its eight legs, and for thread it was using its own spider web, which came out of its mouth.

Yosaku looked closely and saw that it was the same spider which he'd saved from the snake. Then Yosaku understood. The spider had been thankful, so that it had wanted to do something to help Yosaku. It had turned itself into a beautiful young girl and come to weave cloth for him. Just by eating the cotton in the weaving room it could spin it into thread inside its own body, and then with its eight legs it could weave the thread into cloth very, very fast.

Yosaku was grateful for the spider's help. He saw that the cotton was almost used up. So next morning he set out for the nearest village, on the other side of the mountains, to buy more cotton. He bought a big bundle of cotton and started home, carrying it on his back.

Along the way Yosaku sat down to rest, and the same snake that he'd driven away from the spider came up and slipped inside the bundle of cotton. But Yosaku didn't know anything about this. So he carried the cotton home and gave it to the weaving girl.

She was glad to get the cotton, because she'd now used up all the cotton that was left. So she took it and went to the weaving room.

As soon as the girl was inside the weaving room she turned back into a spider and began eating the cotton very, very fast, just as though it were something delicious, so she could spin it into thread inside her body. The spider ate and ate and ate, and then suddenly, when it had eaten down to the bottom of the bundle – the snake jumped out of the cotton. It opened its mouth wide to swallow the spider. The spider was frightened and jumped out of the window. The snake went wriggling fast after it. And the spider had eaten so much cotton that it couldn't run fast. So the snake gradually caught up with the spider. Again the snake opened its mouth wide to gulp the spider down. But just then, Old Man Sun, up in the sky, had been watching what was happening. He knew how kind the spider had been to Yosaku. So he reached down with a sunbeam and caught hold of the end of the web that was sticking out of the spider's mouth, and he lifted the spider high up into the sky, where the snake could not reach it.

The spider was grateful to Old Man Sun for saving him from the snake. So he used all the cotton that was inside his body to weave beautiful fleecy clouds up in the sky. That's the reason why clouds are soft and white like cotton, and also why both a spider and a cloud are called by the same name in Japan – *Kumo*.

From Japan

The Silent Maiden

Once very long ago, there was a beautiful young maiden called Mepo. She was the daughter of the great chief, Amagogo. Mepo was good and handsome, with skin like black velvet, teeth like flashing pearls, eyes with a dark diamond brightness. Her smile made all who saw her love her. Because of her great beauty she was her father's favourite daughter.

When it came time for Mepo to marry, she went to her father and said, "Father, please do not give me to the first man who offers you a great reward, nor to any man you fancy, but let me choose my own husband. He must be handsome, a valiant warrior, a fine hunter and clever."

"A man like that would make a very good husband indeed. If you are looking for such a man, you may certainly choose for yourself," said the chief.

So word came out to the other villages that the young men of the tribe might pay court to Mepo, the beautiful daughter of the chief, Amagogo. They came from miles around, short men, tall men, lean men, fat men, young men and old men. All of them tried so hard to please the girl that she became very tired of their constant attentions. At last she refused to speak to any of them.

"Daughter, why do you behave so?" asked her father. "Your mother and I are worried because you do not speak." Mepo shook her head wearily and refused to say a word.

Still the young men and the old men came. For weeks the spears stuck into the ground at the door of the chief's house told all who passed by that there were many men visiting Mepo. But she only sat in the centre of the admiring circle and smiled sadly. They brought her gifts of ripe fruit, melons, choice meat, and beads of many colours. But still she refused to speak to anyone or to choose between them.

Finally, her father, tired of this stubborn behaviour, sent out word to the villages that he would give Mepo in marriage to anyone who could make her speak.

In a village faraway across the great river lived a brave young chief of another tribe. His name was Fupajena. He heard of the silent maiden and of her father's offer. He went to the village and asked at the house of Amagogo for permission to meet her. The old chief welcomed him. Such a strong and handsome young man would make a fine husband for his daughter.

"How I hope you can make her speak," said Amagogo. "I'm sure she would be happy with you."

Fupajena was shown into the chief's hut. Mepo looked up wearily from her basket making.

"Great beauty is yours, lovely Mepo," said Fupajena with a low bow. "Will you be my wife?"

Mepo lowered her eyes and refused to say a word.

Fupajena had come a long way to pay court to the beautiful maiden. Amagogo had a bed of skins made for him inside one of the houses and invited him to spend the night.

It was weeding time, for the rains had just passed. Early the next morning Mepo took her hoe and went to weed her maize field.

Fupajena watched her go, then quietly followed. When they reached the field, Fupajena again said to her, "Please, beautiful Mepo, be my wife."

Mepo did not answer, but handed him the hoe and went and sat in the shade of a tree. The young chief began hoeing with quick sure strokes. "Look, Mepo," he called, "I have finished."

Mepo looked at the field. She shouted angrily: "Punda, donkey! You have ruined my crop. You hoed up the maize and left the weeds standing!"

Fupajena threw down the hoe and began to dance and laugh. Mepo became angrier and shouted louder than before. "How could anyone be so stupid?"

In mock fright, the young chief ran towards Amagogo's house. Mepo followed, still shouting. Her father and mother hearing the noise, met them outside. They were overjoyed that someone had made their daughter speak.

After her anger cooled, Mepo knew that Fupajena had been clever enough to make her forget her silence. She gladly went home with him to be his wife and was never silent again.

A tale from East Africa, told by Eleanor B. Heady

The Moon Maiden

There dwelt once on the edge of the forest at the foot of Fujiyama, a bamboo-cutter and his wife. They were honest, industrious people who loved each other dearly, but no children had come to bless them, and therefore they were not happy.

"Ah, husband," mourned the wife, "more welcome to me than cherry blossoms in springtime would be a little child of my own."

One evening she stood on the porch of her flimsy bamboo cottage and lifted her eyes toward the everlasting snows on the top of Fujiyama. Then, with swelling breast, she bowed herself to the ground and cried out to the Honourable Mountain: "Fuji no yama, I am sad because no little head lies on my breast, no childish laughter gladdens our home. Send me, I pray thee, from thine eternal purity, a little one to comfort me."

As she spoke, lo! From the top of the Honourable Mountain there suddenly sparked a gleam of light as when the face of a child is lit by a beaming smile. "Husband, Husband, come quickly," called the good woman. "See, there on the heights of Fujiyama a child is beaming upon me."

"It is but your fancy," said the bamboo-cutter and yet he added, "I will climb up and see what is there." So he followed the trail of silvery light through the forest and up the steep slope where Fujiyama towered white and still above him. At last he stopped below a tall bamboo by the bank of a mountain stream, from whence the glow seemed to come. There, cradled in the branches of the tree, he found a tiny moon-child, fragile, dainty, radiant, clad in flimsy, filmy moon-shine, more beautiful than anything he had ever seen before.

"Ah, little shining creature, who are you?" he called.

"I am Princess Moonbeam," answered the child. "The Moon Lady is my mother, but she has sent me to earth to comfort the sad heart of your wife."

"Then, little Princess," said the man eagerly, "1 will take you home to be our child." So the woodman bore her carefully down the mountain side.

"See, wife," he called, "what the Moon Lady has sent you." Then was the good woman overjoyed. She took the little moon-child and held her close, and the moon-child's little arms went twining about her neck, as she nestled snug against her breast. So was the good wife's longing satisfied at last.

As the years passed by, Princess Moonbeam brought nothing but joy to the woodman and his wife. Lovelier and lovelier she grew. Fair was her face and radiant, her eyes were shining stars and her hair had the gleam of a misty silver halo. About her, too, there was a strange, unearthly charm that made all who saw her love her.

One day there came riding by in state the Mikado himself. He saw how Princess Moonbeam lit up the humble cottage, and loved her. Then the Mikado wanted to take her back with him to court. But now that she was a grown maiden the time had come for her to return to her sky mother, the Lady in the Moon.

"Stay, stay with me on earth!" called the Mikado.

"Stay, stay with us on earth!" called the bamboo-cutter and his wife. Then the Mikado got two thousand archers and set them on guard close about the house and even on the roof, that none might get through to take her. But when the moon rose white and full, a line of light like a silver bridge sprung arching down from heaven to earth and floating along that gleaming path came the Lady from the moon. The Mikado's soldiers stood as though turned to stone. Straight through their midst the Moon Lady passed and bent caressingly down for her long-absent child. She wrapped her close in a garment of silver mist. Then she caught her tenderly in her arms, and led her gently back to the sky.

The Princess Moonbeam was glad to go back home, yet as she went, she wept silvery tears for those she was leaving behind. And lo! Her bright, shining tears took wings and floated away to carry a message of love, that should comfort the Mikado, and her earthly father and mother.

To this very day the gleaming tears of the little Princess Moonbeam are seen to float hither and thither about the marshes and groves of Japan. The children chase them with happy cries and say, "See the fireflies! How beautiful they are!" Then their mothers, in the shadow of Fujiyama, tell the children this story – how the fireflies are shining love messages of little Princess Moonbeam, flitting down to bring comfort to earth from her home in the silver moon.

From Japan

The Invisible Hunter

At the far end of a tiny Indian village, where the rosy light of the rising sun played on the ripples of Neganish Bay, lived an old Indian of the Wabanaki with his three daughters. It was the duty of the two elder girls to keep the wigwam in order, cooking the food and dressing the skins for the family's clothing; but they were lazy and shiftless and left most of the work to the youngest girl. Her father called her Little Wonban which means Little Rising Sun, but she was not joyful like the rising sun. She was thin and sad-eyed and wore shabby clothes. Her elder sisters kicked and pushed her about and made her do most of the work, until she often fell asleep from sheer weariness. Sometimes she would fall asleep over the fire and her face was scarred from the hot cinders. Her long black hair looked dull from the ashes, not shining and sleek like that of her sisters. Since there never seemed to be enough skins when her father came back from the hunt to clothe all of the family, Little Rising Sun had only scraps to wrap about her.

One evening by the fire, the old father told his daughters the story of a mighty warrior and hunter named Te-Am (Great Moose) who lived at the far end of the village. His sister kept his lodge for him, since she was his only living relative.

One day, as Te-Am was walking in the forest, a great Chinu came to protect him and to give him a special gift. With this gift, Te-Am had the power to take on the form of a moose. And with this gift he could also make himself invisible. So it was that none of the maidens in the village had ever seen him, though he was said to be very handsome, and his lodge was always well provided with food and soft furs.

Now the father continued his story. "Te-Am's sister has announced that Te-Am wishes to be married. He will take as his wife the first maiden who can see him. Many maidens have already come to his lodge, but none have been able to see him. Now you, my daughters, may go and try your luck."

As the elder sisters heard their father's story, they became very excited and each wanted to go to the lodge of Te-Am. The next morning the eldest sister dressed herself in her best robes with strings of shells around her neck and walked through the village to the lodge of Te-Am.

Te-Am's sister received her kindly and entertained her in the lodge until sunset. Then, when it was time for Te-Am to return from the hunt, his sister invited the girl to walk with her down the road that led from the forest.

Can be sung: Do you see, do you see my brother?
                 Do you see, do you see him coming?

As soon as she saw her brother approaching, for to her he was always visible, she asked the girl, "Do you see my brother coming?" Although she could not see him, the girl pretended to and said, "Yes, I can see him." – "Tell me," asked Te-Am's sister, "of what is his great bow made?" – "Of birch wood," answered the girl, although she could not see it. By the girl's answer the sister knew she had not seen her brother, but she said to her, "Since you see him, let us go back to the wigwam."

           Do you see, do you see my brother?
           Do you see, do you see him coming?
           or humming a melody.

Back in the wigwam, she invited the girl to be seated on her side of the great fire. Then her brother entered and went to his side of the lodge. As he dropped his catch of game to the ground, the girl could see it. And when he drew off his wet moccasins and handed them to his sister, the girl could see them as soon as they touched the sister's hand. But Te-Am she could not see. Sadly, she gave up and went home again.

The next day the second sister wanted to try her luck. She, too, dressed in her finest robes with strings of shells around her neck and walked through the village to the great lodge of Te-Am. She, too, was greeted kindly by his sister. At sunset, she, too, walked with her down the road to see the great hunter return from the forest with his catch of game.

           Do you see, do you see my brother?
           Do you see, do you see him coming?

Like her sister, she, too, could not see Te-Am, although she also pretended to. When Te-Am's sister asked her, "Do you see my brother coming along the path?" She answered, "Yes, I see him." – "Of what is his great bow made?" asked the sister of Te-Am. "Of ash wood," replied the second sister, although she could not see it. "Since you see my brother, let us go back to the wigwam," said Te-Am's sister.

> Do you see, do you see my brother?
> Do you see, do you see him coming?
> *or humming a melody.*

When Te-Am stepped into the wigwam, the girl could not see him, but again, when his catch of game fell from his shoulder to the ground, she could see it. And when his sister handed him some food to eat, as soon as he touched it, the girl could no longer see it. Finally, she, too, returned to her own wigwam, disappointed.

The two elder sisters talked continuously of the lodge of Te-Am and his sister, until Little Rising Sun decided that she, too, must have a glimpse of that wonderful wigwam. The eldest sister laughed, saying, "How can such a mouse as you hope to see Te-Am, when even we could catch no glimpse of him?"

"Nay," answered Little Rising Sun, "while it may be that I cannot see the mighty hunter, I hope that his sister will receive me and I may catch a glimpse of the beautiful lodge with its rich robes of fur, of which all the maidens speak."

The sisters said no more, but they would not lend Little Rising Sun a dress, and she had to make one of birch bark. Upon her feet she wore her father's old moccasins. Nevertheless, she started out, and did not listen to her sisters' unkind words as they made fun of her strange dress and the misfit moccasins.

"Of course I shall not be able to see Te-Am," she thought, "but just to help prepare his supper and see that wonderful wigwam will be joy enough to remember for many days."

At last she came to the wigwam. While she hesitated at the entrance, the sister of Te-Am saw her and welcomed her in kindly fashion, asking her to sit by the fire. Soon she had her talking about her life at home, but Little Rising Sun said nothing of the unkindness of her sisters to her. At sunset, the two maidens walked towards the forest.

Do you see, do you see my brother?
Do you see, do you see him coming?

When the sister saw her brother coming, she said, "Te-Am is coming. Can you see him yonder on the path?" Looking toward the forest, Little Rising Sun opened her eyes in wonder as she replied, "Yes, I see the shining one."

"Tell me then," replied the sister, "of what is his hunter's bow made that he carries in his hand?"

"It is the rainbow!" whispered Little Rising Sun.

"Ah, then you do truly see my brother," replied his sister. "Now let us hasten home and prepare for his coming." So the two maidens hurried back to the wigwam. There Te-Am's sister filled a basin with warm water and poured into it a sweet smelling liquid from an earthen pot. She bathed Little Rising Sun and washed away the scars from her hands and face until her cheeks began to glow. Then she dressed her in a fine robe of soft white buckskin that was deeply fringed and decorated with quills and beads. She brushed and combed Little Rising Sun's hair until it grew long and shiny, and decorated it with beads and tiny shells.

When she was dressed and ready, Little Rising Sun was told to sit at the brother's side of the wigwam and to take the wife's place on the fur rug near the fire.

Scarcely was she seated when Te-Am entered. Smiling, he looked down at Little Rising Sun, saying, "Wajoolkoos – So we are found, are we?" – "Alajul aa – Yes," answered the girl. Then Te-Am asked her to stay always in his wigwam as his wife, and his sister began to prepare the wedding feast.

Meanwhile, when the father of Little Rising Sun returned home from his hunting and found his youngest daughter gone, he asked her sisters

204

what had become of her. "She went out," they answered, "and though we called her she did not come back and would not obey."

The father was worried and set out to search for her. All through the village he went and finally came to the wigwam of Te-Am, where he could hear the sounds of laughter and rejoicing from within. Stepping inside he found his daughter feasting with Te-Am and his sister. At first he did not recognize his child, but then she ran to him and begged his consent to the marriage. This he gladly gave, counselling her to remain and be a good and dutiful wife. And then they all celebrated together. Little Rising Sun became the wife of the great hunter, Te-Am, and together they lived a long and happy life.

Can be sung: He ga, he ga, he ga – ne he.

A Micmac Native American Legend,
adapted by Susan Howard as a marionette play

Per and Paul and Espen Askelad

There was once a man who had three sons, Per and Paul and Espen Askelad. But he was as poor as a church mouse, and his sons were all he had. So he told the three of them time and again that they would have to go out into the world to earn their bread, for if they stayed at home they had only a life of hunger before them.

Faraway from the poor man's cottage the king had his farm. And right outside the king's windows an oak tree had sprung up and this oak was so mighty and tall that it shut out the light from the king's dwelling. The king had promised gold to anyone who could cut down the oak. But no one could do it because, as soon as one piece was chopped off the trunk, two more grew there on the spot. And the king also wanted a well dug to supply water all the year round. Each of his neighbours owned a well, but he had none and he felt it was a disgrace. To anyone who could dig a well to provide water throughout the year the king had promised other riches, but no one was able to do it because the royal farm was high upon a hill, and whenever they started digging they immediately struck hard rock. Now the king had made up his mind that these tasks must be done. He let it be proclaimed from the church doors all over the land that he would give his daughter in marriage and half his kingdom to the man who could fell the great oak beside his dwelling and make him a well providing water throughout the year.

I can assure you that there were many who were anxious to try their luck, but for all their hacking and chopping and all their burrowing and digging they got no further. Every stroke made the oak thicker and thicker, and the rocky hillside showed no sign of getting any softer. The time came when the three brothers wished to set out and try their fortune too. Their father was well pleased, for he thought that even if they did not win the princess and half the kingdom they might find service in the household of a worthy man, and that was as much as he could hope. So when the brothers made up their minds to go to the king's farm, their father gave his consent at once, and Per and Paul and Espen Askelad set off together.

206

After a while they came to a slope covered with spruce, and beyond it was a tall, steep hill. And far above them they could hear the sound of chopping.

"I wonder what it is we can hear chopping on the hill up there?" said Espen Askelad.

"You're a marvel at wondering!" said Per and Paul.

"I think I'd like to see what it is," said Espen Askelad and off he went.

"What a simpleton you are! Have you never heard a woodcutter at work on a hill?" his brothers shouted after him. He climbed up the hillside and followed the sound of chopping, and at last he found that it came from an axe busily cutting the trunk of a pine-tree.

"Good day," said Espen Askelad. "I see you're busy chopping."

"Yes, I've been here chopping a long, long time waiting for you," answered the axe.

"Well, here I am!" said Espen, and he took the axe and knocked off the handle and packed both axe and handle in his knapsack.

When he joined his brothers below, they teased and laughed at him. "What was the surprise up on the hill!" they asked.

"Oh, it was only an axe we heard," replied Espen.

Having walked on further, they came to a rocky cliff where they could hear the sound of hammering and digging, "I wonder what it is we can hear hammering and digging on the cliff up there?" said Espen Askelad.

"You're such a marvel at wondering," said Per and Paul, "have you never noticed woodpeckers hammering at trees before?"

"Yes, but I'd like to go and see what it is," said Espen. And the more they laughed and made fun of him, the less he cared. He climbed up to the cliff and when he got there he saw a pick hammering and digging.

"Good day," said Espen Askelad. "I see you're hammering and digging all alone."

"Yes," said the pick. "I've been here hammering and digging a long, long time waiting for you."

"Well, here I am!" said Espen once more, and he took the pick and knocked off the handle and put it in his knapsack. Then he walked down to join his brothers.

"You must have seen something wonderful on the cliff up there!" said Per and Paul.

"Nothing special. It was only a pick we heard," answered Espen.

They went on for a while until they came to a brook. By now they were all thirsty after their journey, and they lay down beside the brook to drink.

"Now I wonder where this water is coming from?" said Espen Askelad.

"Now I wonder whether you're quite right in the head?" said both Per and Paul. "If you're not mad already, you'll be mad soon enough with all your wondering about this and that. Where does the brook come from? Have you never seen water flowing from a spring in the ground?"

"Yes, but I'd still like to see where it comes from," said Espen.

He started running upstream, and though his brothers shouted and laughed at him he took no notice and went on running. Much further up, the brook became smaller and smaller. He kept on following it until at last he saw a big walnut out of which the water bubbled and flowed.

"Good day," said Espen once more. "I see you're bubbling and singing all alone."

"Oh yes," said the walnut. "I've been here bubbling and singing a long, long time waiting for you."

"Well, here I am!" said Espen. He took a piece of moss and stuffed it into the hole so that the water could not run out, and he put the walnut in his knapsack and went down again to join his brothers.

"So now you've seen where the water comes from! It must have been a strange sight," said Per and Paul together.

"It was just running out of a hole," said Espen. And the other two laughed and made fun of him once more, but Espen did not let them worry him. "Still, I enjoyed seeing it," he said.

They walked on and they came to the king's farm. But since everyone in the kingdom had heard that they could win the princess and half the kingdom if they cut down the great oak and dug a well for the king, so many had come to try their luck that the oak was twice as huge as it had been to begin with, for you will remember that two new pieces grew for every one that was chopped off. And so the king had now decreed that all those who tried and could not fell the oak should be banished to an island and have their ears cropped.

But the two elder brothers were not afraid of what lay in store, for they were quite sure they could cut down the oak. The eldest brother Per was the first to try his luck. But he fared the same as all the others. For every piece he cut off, two new ones grew instead, and the king's men seized him and cropped his ears and sent him out to the island. Then Paul took his turn, and his lot was the same. After he had hacked two or three times and everyone saw that the oak was growing thicker, the king's men took him and put him on the island and cropped his ears even closer, because they thought he ought to have learnt his lesson.

Then Espen Askelad wanted to try.

"If you are so eager to look like a marked sheep, we can crop your ears at once and spare you further trouble!" said the king, who was angry at the thought of the elder brothers.

"I'd rather like to have a try first," said Espen, so they had to let him.

He brought out the axe from his knapsack and fixed on its handle again. "Hew and cut!" said Espen to the axe. And it chopped and chopped so that the splinters flew and it was not long before the oak lay on the ground. After this Espen took his pick and fastened on the handle. "Dig and delve!" said Espen. And the pick hammered and dug and threw up earth and stones, and there was no stopping the sinking of the well this time. When it was deep and broad enough, Espen Askelad took out his walnut, set it in a corner at the bottom and pulled out the moss. "Bubble and flow!" said Espen, and the water came spouting forth from the hole in the nut and in no time the well was full to the brim.

And so Espen felled the oak that shut out the light from the king's windows and he made a well for the king's farm, and he won the princess and half the kingdom, as the king had promised. But it was just as well for Per and Paul that they had lost their ears, otherwise they would have heard everyone saying over and over again that Espen Askelad had not wondered in vain.

From Norway

The Grey Brown Horse

Once upon a time there lived an old man who had three sons. The two older ones looked after the inn. They spent their money freely and were anxious to look handsome and well turned out. But the youngest, Ivan Simpleton, lived from day to day. He loved to stroll through the woods looking for mushrooms and at home sat on the bench by the stove. When the old man felt that his death was near, he said to his sons: "When I am dead I want you to come to my grave for three nights and bring me bread."

The father was buried. When the first night came, the eldest brother was to go to the grave, but he was too lazy and said to the youngest brother: "Ivan, tonight you go instead of me to our father's grave and in return I'll buy you a cake." Ivan agreed to this. He took bread with him and made his way to the church yard, where he sat down and waited. At midnight the ground opened. His father appeared and asked:

"Who is standing by my grave? Is it you, my eldest son? How is everything in Russia? Are the dogs still barking, are the wolves still howling and are my sons still crying for me?" And Ivan answered: "It is I, your son. Everything is alright in Russia."

The father ate the bread and returned into his grave. Ivan went home and on the way he collected mushrooms. At home his eldest brother asked: "Have you seen father?" – "Yes, I have seen him." – "Did he eat the bread?" – "Yes, he ate his fill."

Then came the second night. Now it was the middle brother's turn to go to the grave, but he also was too lazy, and said: "You go to father's grave instead of me, Ivan, and in return I'll give you a pair of shoes." – "Very well," said Ivan.

Ivan took some bread, went to his father's grave, sat down and waited. At midnight the ground opened, his father appeared and asked: "Who is keeping watch by my grave? Is it you, my second son? Tell me, is everything alright in Russia? Are the dogs still barking, the wolves still howling, and are my sons still crying for me?" And Ivan answered: "It is I, your son. Everything is alright in Russia."

The father satisfied his hunger and returned into his grave. Ivan went home and on the way he gathered mushrooms. The second brother asked: "Did father eat the bread?" – "Yes," said Ivan, "he ate his fill."

On the third night when it was Ivan's turn to go he said to his brothers: "I have been there twice, now you can go for a change, I want to have a good rest." But the two brothers answered: "Now come, Ivan, you know what to do. It's better if you go." – "Very well," said Ivan.

Ivan took the bread and went. At midnight the earth opened and his father appeared. "Who is standing watch by my grave, is it you, my youngest son? Tell me, is everything alright in Russia? Are the dogs still barking, the wolves still howling and are my sons still crying for me?" Ivan answered: "It is I, your son Ivan. Everything is alright in Russia."

After his father had eaten the bread he said: "Only you have done what I requested, you were not afraid to come to my grave for three nights. Go into the open field and call: Grey Brown Horse, oh wise horse, come to me, I am waiting for you, serve me faithfully! And when the horse comes, climb into his right ear and come out of his left ear, and you will become a young gentleman, more handsome than anyone on the earth. Get on the horse and ride wherever you want."

Ivan took the bridle which his father gave him, thanked him and went home. Again on the way he looked for mushrooms. The brothers asked him: "Have you seen father?" – "I saw him," said Ivan. – "Did he eat the bread?" – "Yes, he ate his fill and said that we need no longer go to him."

Now at this time, the King announced throughout the land that all young gentlemen were to go to the King's court. His daughter, Vassilissa the Beautiful, had a palace built on twelve pillars with twelve turrets. In this palace she would sit and wait in the uppermost room, until a man with one leap of his horse would reach her and kiss her lips. This rider, whoever he might be and wherever he might come from, would receive Vassilissa the Beautiful in marriage, along with half her father's kingdom.

Ivan's brothers heard of this and said to one another: "Come, we will try our luck." And they poured out a lot of oats for their brave steeds and prepared to set off. They dressed up smartly and combed their curly locks. Ivan, however, squatted by the stove and begged: "Take me with you, brothers, I would like to try my luck too." – "You lout, you stove squatter, you had better go and pick mushrooms in the woods. The people would only laugh if they saw you."

They swung up onto their stately horses, set their caps dashingly over one ear, let out a whistle and, hey presto! They disappeared into a whirling cloud of dust. Ivan, however, took the bridle and went into the open field. There he called out as his father had bidden him: "Grey Brown Horse, oh wise horse, come to me, I am waiting for you, serve me faithfully!"

Hardly had the words died away, than a horse arrived. Under his hooves the earth trembled, flames shot out of his nostrils and thick smoke poured from his ears. As if he were rooted to the spot he stood in front of Ivan and asked: "What do you request?" Ivan stroked the horse, put on the bridle, crept into one of his ears and when he came out of the other one he stood there, a youth more splendid and handsome than anyone had ever known or ever seen before. He swung himself into the saddle and rode off towards the King's palace. The Grey Brown Horse travelled so fast that the earth trembled, tail and mane swept mountains and valleys, tree and bush bent down trembling.

When Ivan reached the King's court many people were already gathered there. In the palace on twelve pillars, crowned with twelve balconies, sat the Princess Vassilissa the Beautiful high up in the uppermost chamber and waited. The King stepped in front of the door and spoke: "Whichever one of you, good fellows, jumps to the high window on horseback and presses a kiss on the lips of our daughter shall be her husband and will receive half of our kingdom."

Immediately the contest began, but the window was high and no one could reach it. Ivan's brothers tried their luck too. They reached half way up. Now it was Ivan's turn. Ivan took a run, clicked his tongue, cracked his whip, urged his horse upward – only two balconies short of his goal. For the second time he started out, sped into the air and was only one balcony short. He rode his animal in a circle, raced it until it steamed, pressed his spurs into its flanks and, like a fire dart, he flew passed the window. Ivan pressed a kiss on the honeyed lips of the princess and she struck his forehead with her ring to mark her seal.

At that, everyone shouted: "Hold him, hold him fast!" But Ivan was already far away.

He galloped to the distant field, slipped into the left ear of his horse and out of the right one and was once more Ivan Simpleton. He let the horse roam and set off for home. On the way he looked for mushrooms. At home he tied a cloth around his forehead. Climbing onto the stove, he stretched himself out.

Soon his brothers came home and related where they had been and what they had seen!

"Many splendid fellows were there, but one surpassed them all. In one leap his horse reached the princess and he kissed her on the mouth. Everyone saw him come, yet no one saw him go." Ivan, who was lying behind the stove pipe called out: "Wasn't that I?" But the brothers corrected him angrily: "A simpleton can only bleat stupid things. You'd better sit behind the stove and eat up your mushrooms."

Gently Ivan unwound the cloth from his forehead, on which the princess had struck him with the ring. The hut was suddenly filled with flaming brightness. Shocked, the brothers cried: "What are you doing, stupid? Will you set fire to the house over our heads?"

The following day the King invited all the princes and gentry, poor and rich, young and old to a feast. Ivan's brothers dressed up for the feast.

"Take me with you," begged Ivan. – "Where should we take you, you stupid fellow? People would burst out laughing. Sit on the stove and eat your mushrooms!"

The brothers swung onto the back of their strong horses and rode away. Ivan however went on foot. And when he came to the banquet in the King's castle he sat down in the lowest place tucked away in the corner.

Princess Vassilissa the Beautiful walked around. She went from one to the other, offered each guest a bowl full of mead and looked to see who carried her seal on his forehead. She had already offered the mead to all the guests, when she came to Ivan, the last one. A strange feeling crept over her heart when she saw him, he was sooty from head to foot and his hair stuck out on all sides. Princess Vassilissa the Beautiful began to question him: "Who are you? Where do you come from? Why have you bound up your forehead?" – "I have knocked myself," replied Ivan. Then the Princess took off the cloth from his forehead and at that moment light flowed through the whole palace. "My seal," she cried, "here he is, who is meant for me!"

The King came up and said: "He cannot be meant for you, he is dirty from head to toe and is a wretched fellow!" Ivan said to the King: "Allow me to wash myself." So the King gave him permission. Ivan went into the courtyard and called as his father had taught him: "Grey Brown Horse, oh wise horse, come to me, I am waiting for you, serve me faithfully."

And immediately, the horse came leaping up, the earth trembled, flames shot from his nostrils and thick smoke poured from his ears. Ivan crept into the horse's right ear and out of the left one and once again he became the youth, so splendid and handsome as one had never known or seen before. People far and wide opened their eyes in astonishment.

Then the merry banquet became a wedding feast. There is no more to be told than that.

From Russia

215

The Noblest Deed

Once there was a very old man in Guadalajara who was about to die. He wanted to leave a diamond, the only wealth he had, to one of his three sons. But he could not decide which one. He called the three sons into his room, and this is what he told them:

"My sons, I am not a rich man. The only thing I have that is worth much is this diamond. It has been in our family for generations, and I would not want it sold. Because it cannot be sold or divided, I can give it to only one of you. The diamond will go to whichever of you accomplishes the noblest deed in a week's time. Go now. Return in a week to tell me what you have done."

A week passed, and the sons returned. They found their father even weaker than before and unable to leave his bed. He asked each in turn to tell his story.

"My father," said the first son, "I thought and thought of a deed that would be worthy. Finally, this is what I did. I gathered together all my property, divided it in half, and gave one half to the poor people of the city."

The old man shook his head. "Ah, that is a good deed," he said, "but not truly noble. After all, it is every man's duty to be as generous as he can to the poor."

"Padrecito," said the second son, "when I was returning home from work one day, I saw a little girl caught in the swift current of the Rio Grande de Santiago. Though I can hardly swim myself, I jumped into the river and pulled her out. The current was so swift, I almost drowned."

"That, too, is a good deed, and yet not noble," said the father. "Every man should be willing to risk his life for the sake of a child."

Then the third son told his story.

"Father, a wonderful thing happened to me. I was walking high up in the mountains very early one morning. There I saw a man, wrapped tight in a blanket, sleeping at the very edge of a cliff! I could hardly believe my eyes. For if he turned this way or that, if he moved at all in his sleep, the man would be certain to fall over the cliff – thousands of feet to the valley below! I crept closer, as quietly as I could, for I didn't want to startle him. And guess who the man was? Sancho, my bitterest enemy! Many times he had threatened to kill me if he got the chance.

"I moved as close to this man as I could. Gently I put my arms around him. Suddenly his eyes opened and looked into mine. I saw he was afraid. "Do not fear," I said. With that I pulled him toward me and rolled with him, away from the cliff.

"We both stood up, and he said, 'Ay! I came this way last night. It was so dark that I could not see my own feet! I was too tired to go on, so I stepped off the path to sleep. I had no idea where I was! I see now that if I had walked a little farther, or turned in my sleep, I would have become food for the vultures in the valley. You have saved my life, amigo – I, who had threatened to kill you!'"

"We threw ourselves into each other's arms and swore to be friends forever. We wept for joy. Each of us found a friend, where before there had been an enemy!"

"Ah, my son!" exclaimed the old man. "That is a beautiful story, and a truly noble deed. It is a rare man who will risk his life for the sake of his enemy. A *noble* man. The diamond is yours!"

A Mexican tale retold by Grant Lyons

The Little Jug

When Mother Holle was still walking across the land there lived a poor widow all alone. Her child had died and the widow cried her eyes sore day and night.

Once, in the evening of Holle Day the widow walked across the fields to the neighbouring village. The moon stood in the sky like a large piece of gold and filled path and fields, bushes and trees with a soft twilight glow. But the widow did not see the beauty around her because her eyes were dim and dull like two wells in which the otter had rummaged. Only her ears were gateways through which what was around her could enter. And so it was that in the night wind she heard soft music and whispers like little voices of a heavenly whirl.

Then the widow saw across the fields a crowd she had not seen before. It was Mother Holle and her little souls. With a chirping song they moved past the widow across the open field, over the hedgerow and straight into the woods.

Mother Holle had already reached the muffled fir trees when one little soul tip-toed slowly across the cold snow. It carried a heavy earthenware jug. When the little one reached the hedge the others had long since passed it. And so it ran hither and thither and looked for a hole through which it could slip. Then the widow recognised her own child and her heartbeat quickened.

She called it by its name but the little soul did not listen. She took it by the hand but it did not recognise the widow. She took it to her heart and wept many tears. And then, when bitter mother-tears wetted the eyes of the little one, the wee mouth spoke as if in a dream:

> "Oh, how warm
> Is mother's arm."

"Oh, child," asked the widow, "will you now come and stay with your mother in her house?"

Said the child: "Dearest Mother, lay aside your sorrow and stay your weeping. The tears which you shed flow over my grave and into this jug. And it is now my lot to drag the jug along. Look, my shift is splashed wet because the jug has overflowed. And the children always run ahead of me. Please, let me go now. Mother Holle is also good and kind. She says: 'Your mother will be with us.' Then we will all be cared for in Mother Holle's land. So, leave go of your weeping and give me rest and yourself peace."

Then the widow lifted her beloved child over the fence, wept once more with all her heart, kissed the pale wee mouth and with her eyes followed the white shift until far away it had disappeared into the light-filled heavenly whirl.

Whenever sorrow overcame the widow and her eyes threatened to overflow she pictured the earthenware jug and the fence, and she stemmed her tears. And so she learned to live in peace.

From Germany

219

Recommended Reading

A is for Ox, B. Sanders ISBN 0 679 74285 9 Vintage Books
Failure to Connect, J. Healy ISBN 0 684 85539 9 Simon & Schuster
Set Free Childhood, M. Large. ISBN 1 903458 43 9 Hawthorn Press
Rudolf Steiner - Life, work, inner path and social intentions, R. Lissau
    ISBN 1 869890 06 X Hawthorn Press
Lifeways, G. Davy & B. Voors ISBN 0 950706 24 8 Hawthorn Press
The Spiritual Tasks of the Homemaker, M. Schmidt-Brabant
    ISBN 0 904693 84 8 Temple Lodge Press, England
Education Towards Freedom ISBN 0 906155 32 0 Lanthorn Press, England
Work and Play in Early Childhood, F. Jaffke
    ISBN 0 86315 227 9 Floris Books, Edinburgh, Scotland
Festivals, Family and Food, D. Carey & J. Large
    ISBN 1 950706 23 X Hawthron Press
Festivals Together, S. Fitzjohn, M. Weston & J. Large
    ISBN 1 869890 46 9 Hawthorn Press
Understanding Children's Drawings, M. Strauss
    Rudolf Steiner Press, England
The Wisdom of Fairytales, R. Meyer ISBN 0 86315 208 2 Floris Books
A Guide to Child Health, M. Glöckler & W. Goebel
    ISBN 0 86315 390 9 Floris Books
Education as Preventive Medicine – A Salutogenic Approach,
    M Glöckler ISBN 0 945803 63 X Rudolf Steiner College Press, USA.
Between Form and Freedom, B Staley ISBN 1 869890 08 6 Hawthorn Press
Brothers and Sisters, K. König ISBN 0 86315 446 8 Floris Books
The Challenge of the Will, Margret Meyerkort & Rudi Lissau
    ISBN 0 945803 41 9 Rudolf Steiner College Press, California, USA
The Oxford Nursery Songbook,
    ISBN 0 19 330193 8 Oxford University Press
The Oxford Dictionary of Nursery Rhymes
    ISBN 0 19 860088 7 Oxford University Press

Let us Form a Ring, Acorn Hill Children's Centre,
    Silver Spring, MD, USA
The Book of 1000 Poems ISBN 0 00 185508 5 Collins Educational
English Fairy Tales, J. Jacobs ISBN 0 679 42809 7 Everyman's Library
The Complete Grimm's Fairy Tales ISBN 0 394 70930 6 Pantheon Books
Milly Molly Mandy Books, J. Brisley, Puffin Books
Seven-Year-Old Wonder Book, I. Wyatt ISBN 0 86315 527 8 Floris Books

Acknowledgements

Further to the acknowledgement on page 3 of this book, the following is a list of permissions granted to reproduce previously published copyright material. Where it has not been possible to locate the original copyright holder, we tender our apologies to any owner whose rights may have been unwittingly infringed.

Mama, oh, mama, come wash my face – titled *Cleano* – by Woody Guthrie, copyright 1954 Folkways Music Publishers, Inc., New York, assigned to Kensington Music Ltd, London SW10 OSZ. From Mrs E Matterson and Penguin Books we are grateful for their kind permission to reproduce the following from This Little Puffin: *Chip chop, choppity chop; Mummy has scissors; Slice, slice the bread; Stepping over stepping stones; There's a cobbler and Two Little boats.* From HarperCollins Publishers Ltd, we are grateful to reproduce the following items from the Book of 1000 Poems: *My Wellington boots go* – titled *Boots and Shoes* – by Lilian McCrea; *Sing a song of washing-up* – titled *The Washing up song* – by Elizabeth Gould; *Bread is a lovely thing to eat* – titled *Lovely Things* – by H. M. Sarson; *Sing a song of mince meat* – titled *Mince meat* – by Elizabeth Gould; *Tinkle, tinkle, tinkle* – titled *The Muffin Man's Bell* – by Ann Hawkshawe; *Bring me a letter* – titled *The Postman* – by Alice Todd; *I am going to market* – titled *Marketing* – by E. J. Falconer, and *Big feet, Black feet* – titled *Feet* by Irene Thompson. *Clink, clink clinkety-clink* – titled *The Milkman* – by Clive Sausom, and reprinted with permission from A & C Black (Publishers) Ltd., from Speech Rhymes. *Shuna dear, come dance with me*, music by J. Knierim and reprinted from Quintenlieder with the kind permission of Rudolf Steiner College Press, California. *The Gift of the Holy Man* and *Four Friends* from Pakistan Folk Tales, published by Hippocrene Books, Inc., New York, 1998. *The Coat and the Ram* from More Russian Picture Tales by Valery Carrick, translated by Nevill Forbes, published by Dover Publications, Inc., Mineola, New York, and reprinted here with the kind assistance of Dover Publications, Inc. *The Grateful Statues, The Sticky, Sticky Pine* and *The Spider Weaver* reproduced with permission from Japanese Children's Favorite Stories, edited by Florence Sakade, published by Charles E. Tuttle Co., Inc. of Boston, Massachusetts and Tokyo, Japan. *The Story of the Shining Princess* printed with permission of Terry Berger. *The Noblest Deed* reproduced from Tales the People Tell in Mexico and printed with the permission of Grant Lyons.

Wynstones Press

Wynstones Press publishes and distributes a range of books, including many titles for children, parents and teachers.

Also available is a wide selection of postcards, folded cards and prints reproduced from original work by a variety of artists. Included amongst these are many works by David Newbatt, who illustrated the covers for this book.

Wynstones Press also distributes a selection of beautifully illustrated Advent Calendars, from publishers in Europe.

For further information please contact:

Wynstones Press
Ruskin Glass Centre
Wollaston Road
Stourbridge
West Midlands DY8 4HE.
England.

Telephone: +44 (0) 1384 399455
Email: info@wynstonespress.com
Website: wynstonespress.com